THE GARDEN LOVER'S
QUIZ & PUZZLE
BOOK

THE GARDEN LOVER'S
QUIZ & PUZZLE
BOOK

**More than 1000 teasers to delight
the green fingered**

AURA

This edition published in 2016
by Baker & Taylor (UK) Limited,
Bicester, Oxfordshire, OX26 4ST

Copyright © Arcturus Holdings Limited
26/27 Bickels Yard, 151–153 Bermondsey Street
London SE1 3HA

Puzzles Copyright © Puzzle Press Ltd

ISBN: 978-1-78599-697-9
AD005177UK

Printed in China

INTRODUCTION

The puzzles and quizzes presented in the *Garden Lover's Puzzle and Quiz Book* have been specially devised to present an entertaining variety of puzzles and quizzes with a natural flavour.

Whatever your taste in puzzles and quizzes, we are sure you will find this selection challenging and fun.

Solutions to all of the puzzles and quizzes can be found at the back of the book, but try not to peek!

1 True or False Maze

Each leaf contains either a true statement or a false statement, and your task is to begin at the one marked 'START', following a continuous line, travelling from leaf to touching leaf, until you reach the one marked 'END'. Every true statement is used in the path from 'START' to 'END', so there are no shortcuts, no paths may cross, nor can any leaf be used twice in order to reach your destination!

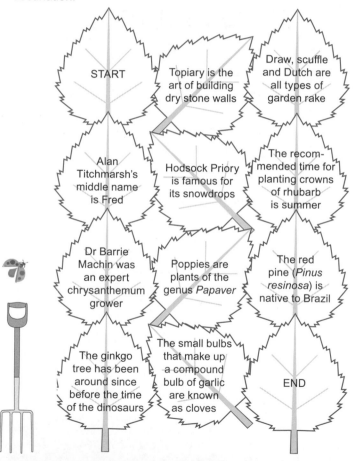

START

Topiary is the art of building dry stone walls

Draw, scuffle and Dutch are all types of garden rake

Alan Titchmarsh's middle name is Fred

Hodsock Priory is famous for its snowdrops

The recommended time for planting crowns of rhubarb is summer

Dr Barrie Machin was an expert chrysanthemum grower

Poppies are plants of the genus *Papaver*

The red pine (*Pinus resinosa*) is native to Brazil

The ginkgo tree has been around since before the time of the dinosaurs

The small bulbs that make up a compound bulb of garlic are known as cloves

END

2 General Knowledge

See how many of the questions below you can correctly answer.

1 Often used to flavour gin, what name is commonly given to the fruit of the blackthorn, *Prunus spinosa*?

2 The carnation, pink, and sweet william belong to which genus of flowering plants?

3 Who was the Roman goddess of fertility and flowers?

4 What is studied by an arborist?

5 'Chinatown', 'Arthur Bell', 'Sweet Remembrance' and 'Mountbatten' are all roses that bear blooms of which colour?

6 Born in Sweden in 1707, which eminent naturalist created the binomial system of naming plants and animals?

7 What is the common name for the plant with yellow flowers used as a traditional herbal remedy to relieve the symptoms of low mood and mild anxiety?

8 Edelweiss, a European mountain plant, translates from German to English as what?

9 What common name is given to *Taxus baccata*?

10 The long-running BBC programme *Gardeners' World* was first broadcast in which decade of the last century?

Quotation

A garden is a grand teacher. It teaches patience and careful watchfulness; it teaches industry and thrift; above all it teaches entire trust.

Gertrude Jekyll

3 General Knowledge

See how many of the questions below you can correctly answer.

1 What name is given to a storage organ consisting of a swollen stem base covered with scale leaves of a plant such as the daffodil, tulip or lily?

2 What is another name for the 'bluebottle' (*Centaurea cyanus*), once commonly seen in fields of cereal crops?

3 Which plant is also called 'old man's beard' and 'traveller's joy'?

4 What name is commonly given to culinary plants such as marjoram, rosemary, oregano, angelica, bergamot and hyssop?

5 Which plant is named after the French phrase 'dent-de-lion', meaning 'lion's tooth'?

6 *Ananas* is the botanical name for which fruit?

7 What term describes increasing humidity in a greenhouse by way of watering the floor surface?

8 What are John Innes 1, 2 and 3?

9 Which two methods are used to start a new lawn?

10 What name is given to the offspring produced by the mating of different species or varieties of plants?

Quotation

Someone's sitting in the shade today because someone planted a tree a long time ago.

Les Brown

8

Identity Parade

4

Match the silhouettes of these leaves to the names of the trees on which they grow, as given in the list below.

1

2

3

4

5

6

ACACIA   **LILAC**
CHESTNUT   **ROWAN**
HAWTHORN   **SUGAR MAPLE**

Place the letters of each word, one per cell, so that every word flows in a clockwise direction around a number.

Where the hexagons of one word overlap with those of another, the letter in each cell is common to both.

When finished, rearrange the letters in the pale green hexagons to form the name of a fruit.

CORNET

GODWIT

HAIRDO

MAGNUM

REGAIN

REJECT

SAVAGE

SNIPER

SPIRIT

STIGMA

SUMMON

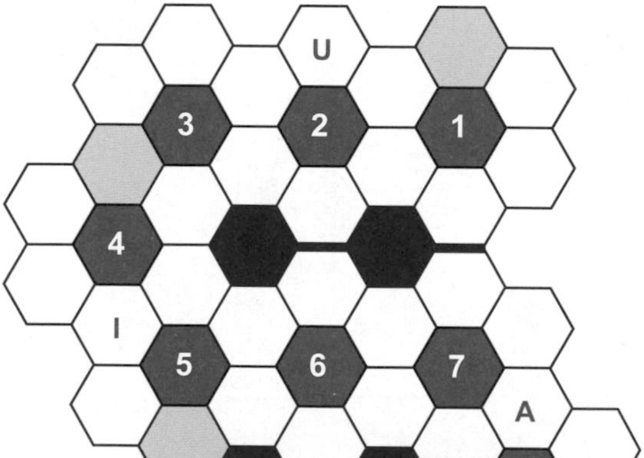

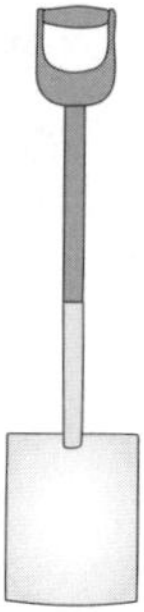

Answer: _____

6) Plants in Music

See how many of the questions below you can correctly answer.

1   Which hardy alpine flower appears in the title of a song from *The Sound of Music*?

2   *Le Spectre de la Rose* from the song cycle *Les nuits d'été* was written by which French composer?

3   Sung by Nat King Cole as the theme tune for a film of the same name, which much-recorded song was formerly entitled *Les feuilles mortes* in its original French version?

4   *Tulips from Amsterdam* was a hit for which British entertainer in 1958?

5   Which 'flowery' song was a UK No 2 hit in 1967 for the band The Move?

6   Which four herbs form the title of an album by Simon and Garfunkel?

7   *Waltz of the Flowers* comes from which Tchaikovsky ballet?

8   *Lily the Pink* was a UK No 1 hit for which Liverpool band in 1968?

9   The 'Flower Duet' from the opera *Lakme* by Delibes was for many years used in TV adverts for which major airline?

10 In the film *2001: A Space Odyssey* which 'flower song' does the malfunctioning computer, Hal, sing as 'he' is disconnected from the spacecraft's systems?

7 General Knowledge

See how many of the questions below you can correctly answer.

1 Which vegetable comes in varieties of 'crisphead' and 'butterhead'?

2 What is the term for the cutting back of surplus growth in order to allow new growth?

3 Timothy, fescue and Yorkshire fog are all types of what?

4 Sweet potatoes, pumpkins and carrots are high in which vitamin, for which retinol is the chemical name?

5 What is the common name of *Papaver somniferum*?

6 A formicary would be home to what kind of insects?

7 What is the colour of a tansy's button-like flowers?

8 Because it opens in the morning and closes at night, which flower gets its name from 'dæges eage', meaning 'day's eye'?

9 What is the common English name for the succulent plant *Sempervivum*?

10 With their colourful heads and cone-like fruits, Banksias were named after Sir Joseph Banks, who collected specimens and brought them to Europe from which country?

Quotation

A weed is a plant that has mastered every survival skill except for learning how to grow in rows.

Doug Larson

8 Wordladder

Change one letter at a time (but not the position of any letter) to make a new word – and move from the word at the top of the ladder to the word at the bottom using the exact number of rungs provided.

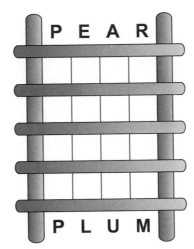

P E A R

P L U M

9 True or False

Can you decide whether the statement below is true or false?

The flowers of the corn cockle range from mid- to deep blue in colour.

True or **False**

13

10 Food and Drink

See how many of the questions below you can correctly answer.

1 What is the name of the tree of the genus *Acer* from whose sap sugar and syrup can be made?

2 Of which fruit are there 'maraschino' and 'morello' varieties?

3 The distilled sap of which plant is used to make tequila?

4 Which variety of celery is grown for its turnip-like edible root?

5 Which vegetable's botanical name is *Nasturtium officinale*?

6 'Camus de Bretagne', 'Vert de Laon' and 'Jerusalem' are all varieties of which vegetable?

7 By what name is the fruit of the carambola tree more commonly known?

8 In cookery, the term 'florentine' means served with which vegetable?

9 Lemons, limes and oranges belong to which genus of trees?

10 What name is given to a type of orange, either a variety of tangerine or a hybrid of orange and tangerine?

Quotation

Gardens are not made by singing "Oh, how beautiful", and sitting in the shade.

Rudyard Kipling

11 Petal Puzzle

How many words of three or more letters can you make from those on the petals, without using plurals, abbreviations or proper nouns? The central letter must appear once in every word and no letter may be used more than once unless it is on a different petal. There is at least one nine-letter word to be found.

General Knowledge

See how many of the questions below you can correctly answer.

1 Which common plant is often found where nettles thrive and can be used to alleviate the irritation of nettle stings?

2 What is the more common name for the Belladonna plant?

3 Which South American herb is used to make a treatment for digestive disorders and is commonly used as a flavouring in cocktails?

4 To which genus do forget-me-nots belong?

5 Which poisonous plant related to the potato, was so-named because it was considered to be especially dangerous to poultry?

6 What do the pitcher plant, bladderwort and sundew plant all have in common?

7 What is a stolon?

8 Which herb gives Earl Grey tea its distinctive flavour?

9 What is the common English name for the plant genus *Veronica*?

10 What is the English name of *Primula veris*, a common meadow flower, also known in the West Country as 'Bunch of Keys'?

Quotation

Flowers don't worry about how they're going to bloom. They just open up and turn toward the light, and that makes them beautiful.

Jim Carrey

13 Garden Borders

Fit the letters G, A, R, D, E and N into the grid in such a way that each horizontal row, each vertical column and each of the heavily bordered sections of six squares contains a different letter. Some letters are already in place.

			A		
G			R		E
E	G				D
		G		N	
	N			G	A

14 Spring Flowers Tracker

Starting at the top left corner and ending at the bottom right, track a path from letter to letter, in any direction except diagonally, in order to find the hidden spring flowers. All of the letters must be used once only.

A	S	N	O	W	D	L	O	V	E	L	L	E	B	H	Y	A
N	E	N	P	O	R	G	X	E	H	C	E	R	O	P	I	C
E	M	O	C	E	L	A	O	F	E	O	W	S	L	I	N	T
L	L	I	T	F	S	N	D	I	N	I	D	F	A	A	L	H
A	L	I	I	R	U	C	O	R	C	L	O	F	D	C	I	L
R	U	P	O	L	F	R	S	I	R	I	O	S	L	U	E	L
Y	T	V	I	E	T	E	E	A	P	M	R	E	B	E	B	L

17

Spot the Same

Which two potted plants are identical in every detail?

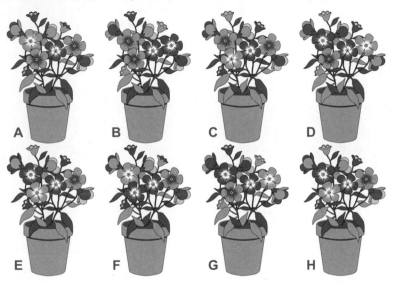

A B C D

E F G H

16 Spelling Bee

Which is the only one of the following to be correctly spelled?

a RHODADENDRON

b RHODODENDRON

c RHODODENDRUN

d RHODIDENDRUM

17 The Natural World

Find the correct answer to each question from the four alternatives.

1 Aconite is a potent poison that is most often derived from wolf's bane and which other common plant?
  a. Cuckoo pint
  b. Foxglove
  c. Monkshood
  d. Rue

2 Which is the world's largest desert?
  a. Kalahari
  b. Gobi
  c. Atacama
  d. Antarctica

3 Agriculture started around 9,500 BC, in an area known as the Fertile Crescent. What ancient land was at the centre of this region?
  a. Scythia
  b. Mesopotamia
  c. Nubia
  d. Barbaria

4 Which ape's name translates as 'man of the forest'?
  a. Orang-utan
  b. Gorilla
  c. Mandrill
  d. Chimpanzee

5 What is most abundant gas in Earth's atmosphere?
  a. Oxygen
  b. Argon
  c. Nitrogen
  d. Carbon dioxide

6 One of the world's longest rivers, the Yenisei lies mainly in which country?
  a. Canada
  b. China
  c. Argentina
  d. Russia

7 Seen travelling above the Himalayas, which is the world's highest-flying goose?
  a. Bar-headed goose
  b. Snow goose
  c. Canada goose
  d. Swan goose

General Knowledge

See how many of the questions below you can correctly answer.

1 With purple flowers and fern-like foliage, in which season of the year does the pasque flower (*Pulsatilla vulgaris*) bloom?

2 By what other name is the sea pink (*Armeria maritima*) known?

3 'London pride' is a common garden hybrid of which plant that grows in rocky terrain in the wild?

4 What creature constructs and lives in a drey?

5 To which genus of plants does the Transvaal daisy belong?

6 'Celestial', 'Alba Maxima' and 'Maiden's Blush' are all varieties of which flower?

7 What vegetable was the first to be canned and sold commercially?

8 What is the medical name for nettle rash, or hives?

9 Which underground plant stem is also known as a rootstock?

10 Commonly found in arid regions, with fleshy stems and leaves swollen with water-storage tissues, which is the largest family of succulent plants?

Quotation

I grow plants for many reasons: to please my eye or to please my soul, to challenge the elements or to challenge my patience, for novelty or for nostalgia, but mostly for the joy in seeing them grow.

David Hobson

Garden Maze

How successful will you be in trying to find a route to the centre of this garden maze?

20 Salad Sudoku

Every row, every column and each of the nine smaller boxes of nine squares should be filled with a different number from 1 to 9 inclusive. Some numbers are already in place. When the grid is completely filled, decode the numbers in the shaded squares, then rearrange the letters to spell out the name of a salad vegetable or fruit.

		8					7	6
6				5				
			7	2		3		
8		5		1	3			
4	7						2	3
			4	6		5		8
	1		8	4				
				2				7
9	4					1		

Code

1	2	3	4	5	6	7	8	9
A	C	E	L	R	S	T	U	Y

Answer: _____

22

General Knowledge

See how many of the questions below you can correctly answer.

1 What group of organisms includes mushrooms, toadstools, moulds, rusts and yeasts?

2 How is the rose-bay shrub (or rose-laurel shrub) otherwise known?

3 What name is given to the propagation method in which part of one tree or shrub is transferred onto another?

4 Which is the tallest grass plant in the world?

5 Grasslands cover approximately what percentage of the Earth's land area: 10 per cent, 20 per cent, or 40 per cent?

6 What name is given to the bitter aromatic resinous exudate from the stem of various Arabian and African trees of the genus *Commiphora*?

7 An entomophobe fears which small creatures?

8 A spiny and dense evergreen shrub with fragrant golden-yellow flowers, what plant is also known as whin, or furze?

9 Usually grown as a pot plant, what is the common name for *Saintpaulia*?

Quotation

What a man needs in gardening is a cast-iron back, with a hinge in it.

Charles Dudley Warner

General Knowledge

See how many of the questions below you can correctly answer.

1 Which garden machine was invented in 1830 by Edwin Beard Budding, an engineer from Stroud in Gloucestershire?

2 Which insects are of the order *Coleoptera*?

3 Which insect is a smaller, more slender relative of the dragonfly?

4 What is the rather breezy alternative name for the common anemone?

5 Herb Paris (*Paris quadrafolia*) bears a black berry: is it suitable for human consumption?

6 Queen Elizabeth I allegedly had a phobia of which flowers?

7 Silkworms prefer to eat the leaves of which bush?

8 Entomology is the study of what forms of life?

9 What name is given to the projecting piece on a sundial that shows the time by the position of its shadow?

10 What serious disease of roses is caused by a fungus, *Diplocarpon rosae*, that infects the leaves and greatly reduces plant vigour?

Quotation

It is like the seed put in the soil - the more one sows, the greater the harvest.

Orison Swett Marden

23 Shape-up

Every row and column in this grid originally contained one bird, one flower, one leaf, one mushroom and two blank squares, although not necessarily in that order. Every symbol with a black arrow refers to the first of the four symbols encountered in the direction of the arrow. Every symbol with a white arrow refers to the second of the four symbols encountered in the direction of the arrow. Can you complete the original grid?

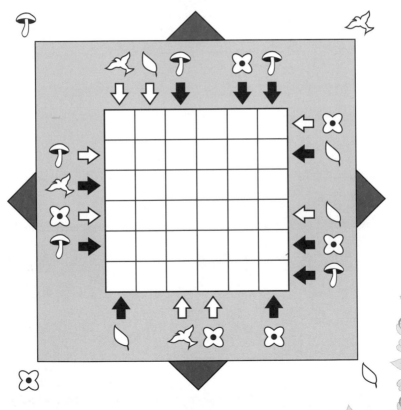

24 What's It Worth?

Each symbol stands for a different number. In order to reach the correct total at the end of each row and column, what is the value of the bird, flower, leaf and mushroom?

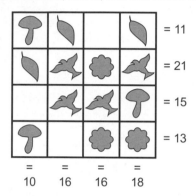

25 Shape Spotter

Which is the only shape to appear twice in exactly the same shading (black, white or green) in the box below? You'll need a keen eye for this one, as some shapes overlap others!

26 The Capable Mr Brown

Find the correct answer to each question from the four alternatives.

1   Capability Brown's first landscape commission was for a lake in the park at Kiddington Hall. In which English county is Kiddington Hall?

2   One of Capability Brown's sayings (a phrase coined by William Kent), which he generally applied to his landscape design projects, was that "Nature abhors…" what?

3   Landscaped by Brown during the 1750s, which West Sussex park has the largest herd of fallow deer in England?

4   Brown famously remarked that he wouldn't accept commissions to work in Ireland. For what reason?

5   For which Worcestershire mansion was the first architectural remodelling commission given to Brown?

6   Often described as the last of the great English garden designers of the 18th century, which landscape architect was Brown's successor at Sheffield Park, East Sussex, during the late 1780s?

7   To which Buckinghamshire estate was Brown appointed head gardener in 1741?

8   In 1764, which king appointed Brown to the position of Master Gardener at Hampton Court Palace?

9   Vanbrugh's Grand Bridge was partly submerged by Brown's scheme to landscape the park and gardens at which Oxfordshire country manor?

10   In 2015, the Duchess of Rutland announced the implementation of a scheme drawn up by Brown more than 230 years before to landscape the surrounds of which Leicestershire castle?

General Knowledge

See how many of the questions below you can correctly answer.

1 What type of fruit or vegetable is a gherkin?

2 Which gas is commonly called 'marsh gas'?

3 What name is given to the female organ of a flower?

4 Which garden pest is also known as a 'thunder fly'?

5 Which plant of the marigold genus was formerly used in plasters, etc, for the healing of wounds?

6 In gratitude for Britain's help during World War II, which country presents the annual gift of a Christmas tree that stands in Trafalgar Square?

7 Which plant with finely-divided leaves is also called yarrow?

8 Identify the correct spelling:
A. photosynthisis
B. photosynthesis
C. photosynthises

9 'Devil's arrow' and 'Devil's darning needle' are alternative names for which flying insect?

10 What kind of creature is a 'garden tiger'?

Quotation

Who loves a garden loves a greenhouse too.

William Cowper

The object of this puzzle is to trace a single path from the top left square to the bottom right square of the grid, moving through all of the cells in either a horizontal, vertical or diagonal direction. Every cell must be entered once only and your path should take you through the letters in the sequence V-I-N-E-V-I-N-E, etc. Can you find the logical way through?

V	E	V	N	V	I	N	E
I	N	I	I	E	I	V	V
N	V	E	V	E	N	E	I
E	I	N	N	I	E	V	N
N	V	I	N	I	V	I	N
V	E	V	E	I	I	V	E
I	N	N	N	I	N	I	N
E	V	I	E	V	E	V	E

See how many of the questions below you can correctly answer.

1 What are prunes made from?

2 'Ailsa Craig' and 'Moneymaker' are popular varieties of which fruit?

3 *Hypericum* is better-known as which plant that, when used medicinally, produces an anti-depressant effect?

4 What is a nickname for the crane fly, a long-legged two-winged fly of the family *Tipulidae*?

5 What is a 'White Lisbon'?

6 Which vegetable has varieties including 'purple sprouting' and 'calabrese'?

7 What is often used on fruit and vegetables to correct a magnesium deficiency?

8 With a long root like that of a parsnip and allied to the scorzoneras, what plant (*Tragopogon porrifolius*) is also known as the 'vegetable oyster'?

9 Which is the chief mineral found in bananas?

10 A vespiary would be home to which kind of insect?

Quotation

Flowers are the sweetest things God ever made, and forgot to put a soul into.

Henry Ward Beecher

30 Riddle-Me-Ree

Find one letter per line, following the clues given in the verse below. For example, 'My first is in houses, but never in homes' gives the letter U as the first letter. When you have finished, the letters will spell another word.

My first's in DIANTHUS, and but not found in PINK,

My second's in CHAIN, but never in LINK,

My third's in CALCIUM, though not in CHALK,

My fourth Is in STEM, and also in STALK,

My fifth is in RYE, but not seen in CORN,

My whole is a plant you might see in a lawn.

1st	2nd	3rd	4th	5th

31 True or False

Can you decide whether the statement below is true or false?

A rhizome is an underground stem producing roots and leafy shoots.

True or False

Use the telephone dial in order to spell out a quotation attributed to May Sarton.

4 3 5 6   9 8   8 6   1 3   3 9 3 7   3 1 4 8 4 3 9 5

3 1 7 2 3 6 3 7 8   6 3   8 4 3   8 6 4 7 4 8 ,   9 4 6

4 6 6 9   8 4 1 8   9 4 8 4 6 9 8   2 1 7 4 6 3 8 8

6 6 8 4 4 6 3   2 6 5 3 8   8 6   1 4 7 8 4 ,   1 6 2

9 4 8 4 6 9 8   5 4 3 4 8   6 6 8 4 4 6 3   3 5 6 9 3 7 8 .

33 Multiple Choice

Find the correct answer to each question from the four alternatives.

1 *Allium cepa* is the Latin name for which common vegetable?
  a. Parsnip   **b.** Potato
  c. Onion   **d.** Asparagus

2 Also called moneywort, the trailing loosestrife (*Lysimachia nummularia*) is also known as creeping …
  a. Jenny   **b.** Penny
  c. Wenny   **d.** Benny

3 The word 'anemophily' refers to pollination by what means?
  a. Wind   **b.** Hummingbirds
  c. Butterflies or moths   **d.** Water

4 Popular at Christmas, to which plant genus do poinsettias belong?
  a. *Eriogonum*   **b.** *Euphorbia*
  c. *Echinacea*   **d.** *Erica*

5 St Germain liqueur is made from the flowers of which tree?
  a. Hawthorn   **b.** Elder
  c. Horse chestnut   **d.** Crab apple

6 The excrement or other refuse of wood-boring larvae is called …
  a. Fraim   **b.** Fratch
  c. Frass   **d.** Frater

7 What is the name more commonly given to *Helleborus niger* that bears white flowers in winter or early spring?
  a. Poinsettia   **b.** Snowdrop
  c. Amaryllis   **d.** Christmas rose

8 An easy-to-grow evergreen shrub with spikes of scented flowers, lavender is a member of which family of plants?
  a. Rosemary   **b.** Parsley
  c. Mint   **d.** Sage

34 The Bible

See how many of the questions below you can correctly answer.

1 "I am the ___, the lily of the valleys. As the lily among the thorns, so is my love among the daughters." These sentences are from the Bible, Song of Solomon 2:1-2. What three words (the name of a plant) are missing?

2 What plant is missing from this verse of the Bible, Matthew 13:31: "Another parable put he forth unto them, saying, The kingdom of heaven is like to a grain of ___ seed, which a man took, and sowed in his field."?

3 "Woe unto you, scribes and Pharisees, hypocrites! for ye pay tithe of ___ and anise and cummin, and have omitted the weightier matters of the law, judgment, mercy, and faith: these ought ye to have done, and not to leave the other undone." Which herb is missing from this quotation from Matthew 23:23?

4 In Exodus 3:2 to whom did the angel of the Lord appear in a flame of fire out of the midst of a bush?

5 What kind of birds arrived to sustain the Israelites just before the sending of manna?

6 Fill in the missing word (a herb): "Purge me with ___, and I shall be clean: wash me, and I shall be whiter than snow" (Psalms 51:7).

7 From the wood of which tree were the Israelites instructed to make the Ark of the Covenant?

8 In which garden near Jerusalem was Jesus betrayed by Judas Iscariot?

9 Which famous gardens were part of the palace of King Nebuchadnezzar II?

10 Which gift of the Wise Men to Jesus was obtained from trees of the genus *Boswellia*?

35 Spidoku

Each of the eight segments of the spider's web should be filled with a different number from 1 to 8, in such a way that every ring also contains a different number from 1 to 8.

The segments run from the outside of the spider's web to the centre, and the rings run all the way around.

Some numbers are already in place. Can you fill in the rest?

36 Latin List

Pair up each of the numbered boxes on the left with the lettered boxes on the right to match the common names of plants with their botanical (or 'Latin') names.

| 1 | Silver birch | a | *Narcissus* |

| 2 | Deadly nightshade | b | *Lavatera* |

| 3 | Daffodil | c | *Quercus robur* |

| 4 | Sunflower | d | *Atropa belladonna* |

| 5 | Mallow | e | *Erica* |

| 6 | Poppy | f | *Helianthus* |

| 7 | Heath | g | *Betula pendula* |

| 8 | English oak | h | *Papaver* |

Number	Letter
1	
2	
3	
4	

Number	Letter
5	
6	
7	
8	

General Knowledge

See how many of the questions below you can correctly answer.

1 Sometimes seen in the garden, what kinds of mammals comprise the order *Chiroptera*?

2 What name is given to the larva of an insect with incomplete metamorphosis, such as the dragonfly or mayfly?

3 'Arran Pilot', 'Pentland Javelin' and 'Maris Bard' are all varieties of which vegetable?

4 Of which genus are cabbages, broccoli and cauliflowers?

5 Which common spring flower has the Latin name *Narcissus pseudonarcissus*?

6 In the northern hemisphere, spring lasts from the vernal equinox on 20 March to what, on 20-21 June?

7 Which order of insects has the greatest number of species?

8 What are the leaves of ferns and palm trees called?

9 Which common yellow meadow flower is of the genus *Ranunculus*?

10 What word describes plants that complete their life-cycle within one year?

Quotation

One of the healthiest ways to gamble is with a spade and a package of garden seeds.

Dan Bennett

Find the correct answer to each question from the four alternatives.

1 Which kinds of reptiles comprise the order *Chelonia?*
   a. Turtles and tortoises   **b.** Snakes
   c. Lizards   **d.** Crocodiles

2 What kind of cat is *Felis silvestris*?
   a. Cheetah   **b.** Asian tiger
   c. Ocelot   **d.** Wildcat

3 Of the many kinds of shark in the world's oceans today, which is the largest?
   a. Great white   **b.** Whale shark
   c. Grey reef shark   **d.** Hammerhead

4 Which member of the cat family is the largest by weight?
   a. African lion   **b.** Siberian tiger
   c. Sumatran tiger   **d.** Indonesian tiger

5 What kind of animal is the Komodo dragon?
   a. Alligator   **b.** Crocodile
   c. Lizard   **d.** Gharial

6 Murder, murmuration and parliament are all collective nouns for which types of animal?
   a. Sheep   **b.** Fish
   c. Birds   **d.** Insects

7 Which is Britain's smallest rodent?
   a. Harvest mouse   **b.** Dormouse
   c. Water vole   **d.** Shrew

8 On which Indian Ocean island was the dodo bird rendered extinct in the 17th century?
   a. Mauritius   **b.** Madagascar
   c. Sri Lanka   **d.** Sumatra

39 Round the Block

You won't need a starting block to get you under way, because it isn't a race! Just arrange the six-letter solutions to the clues into the six blocks around each clue number. Write the answers in a clockwise or anticlockwise direction and you'll find that the last answer fits into the first; the main problem will be to decide in which square to put the first letter of each word…

When read in a clockwise direction (not necessarily starting at either of the topmost squares), the letters in the pale green squares spell out the name of a bird you might see in the garden.

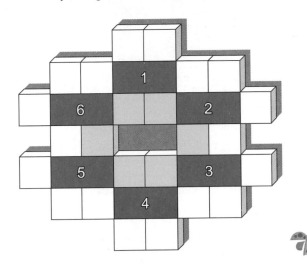

1 Picnic basket

2 Mixed with foreign matter, adulterated

3 Pliant and flexible

4 Again but in a new or different way

5 Sufficient to cause death

6 Hero of a tragedy by Shakespeare

39

40 Casting Shadows

Which one of the shadows is that of the lawnmower shown here?

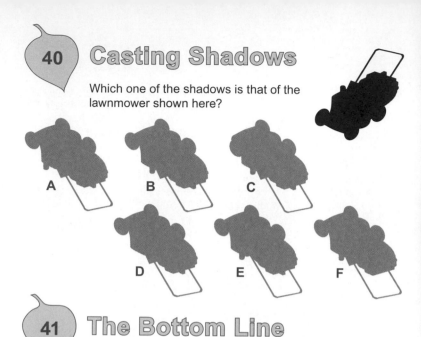

A

B

C

D

E

F

41 The Bottom Line

The bottom line of this grid is waiting to be filled. Every square in the solution contains only one symbol from rows 1 to 5 above, although two or more squares in the solution may contain the same symbol. At the end of every numbered row is a score, which shows:

1 the number of symbols placed in the correct finishing position on the bottom line, as indicated by a tick; and

2 the number of symbols which appear on the bottom line, but in a different position, as indicated by a cross.

Can you fill each square with the correct symbol?

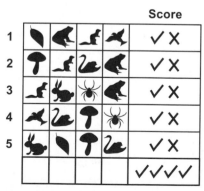

				Score
1				✓ ✗
2				✓ ✗
3				✓ ✗
4				✓ ✗
5				✓ ✗
				✓✓✓✓

42 Multiple Choice

Find the correct answer to each question from the four alternatives.

1 To which genus of plants do lilacs belong?
a. *Echinacea* **b.** *Syringa*
c. *Acer* **d.** *Brassica*

2 Which of the following describes an infection of the roots of cabbages and related plants by *Plasmodiophora brassicae*, a soil-dwelling micro-organism?
a. Club root **b.** Grey mould
c. Dieback **d.** Powdery mildew

3 Cutworms are the larvae of what type of creatures?
a. Dragonflies **b.** Ladybirds
c. Black beetles **d.** Moths

4 'Red Brunswick', 'Autumn Champion' and 'Centurion' are varieties of which vegetable?
a. Carrot **b.** Cauliflower
c. Onion **d.** Potato

5 What nickname was given to the 18th century landscape gardener Lancelot Brown?
a. Competent **b.** Capability
c. Skilful **d.** Perfect

6 A member of the buttercup family, by what name is *Delphinium consolida* better known?
a. Clematis **b.** Globeflower
c. Larkspur **d.** Hollyhock

7 Which one of the following is not a member of the *Allium* genus?
a. Chives **b.** Onion
c. Leek **d.** Beetroot

8 What type of insects are both *Lasius niger* and *Myrmica rubra*?
a. Ants **b.** Aphids
c. Earwigs **d.** Flea beetles

See how many of the questions below you can correctly answer.

1 'Pepinex' and 'Telegraph' are both varieties of which salad vegetable or fruit?

2 Dark green leafy vegetables such as Swiss chard and spinach are good sources of what mineral, a deficiency of which is the main cause of anaemia?

3 What is an 'elf-cup'?

4 What is an arboretum?

5 What is another, more common name for the common heather *Calluna vulgaris*?

6 'Hybrid tea', 'climbing', 'floribunda' and 'miniature' are all types of which garden plant?

7 What is the common name of *Meconopsis cambrica*?

8 What is a pergola?

9 What is the general term for the *Siphonaptera* order of insects?

10 Used in perfumery and formerly in medicine, from which flowering plant is orris root obtained?

Quotation

I think this is what hooks one to gardening: it is the closest one can come to being present at creation.

Phyllis Theroux

In Code

Each letter in the names of these plants is represented by a number which remains the same for that letter wherever it occurs on the page. Work out the code to reveal the common names of the plants. Some numbers are already decoded.

1	2	3	3	4	1	5	6
						I	

7	8	7	7	8	9	10	5	11	12
					R				

13	2	6	6	3	6	4	13	8	9
						O			

14	4	9	15	8	9	2	1	5	15	14
			S							

1	4	16	17	6	2	15
			G			

3	5	9

18	2	11	12	8	9	19	16	9	20

19	8	6	6	15
B				

9	16	11	11	8	9

19	8	2	11

15	13	8	8	12

7	8	2

43

Daffodil Dilemma

Ivor Dibber has been given a plan by his wife, who would like some daffodil bulbs to be planted in a square patch of grass. Mrs Dibber has made a grid map, showing the long-suffering Ivor exactly where the bulbs are to be planted, and she has decided to test Ivor's brain (and patience) by making a puzzle of it…

Those squares containing numbers are empty, but where a number appears in a square, it indicates how many daffodil bulbs are to be planted in the squares (up to a maximum of eight) surrounding the numbered one, touching it at any corner or side. There is only one bulb in any individual square.

Ivor needs your help. Place a circle into every square that should contain a daffodil bulb.

				2	2	2			
3		4	2	2			4	2	
1			2		3				0
	3	4				2		1	
1		2		2			0		0
2			1						
	2				2	3			0
			3	3	3			2	0
0	2	2	3						1
					2	2		2	

Multiple Choice

Find the correct answer to each question from the four alternatives.

1 How is the *Convolvulus* genus of plants also known?
- **a.** Periwinkle
- **b.** Bindweed
- **c.** Honeysuckle
- **d.** Daisy

2 In which English county is the Vale of Eden?
- **a.** Kent
- **b.** Worcestershire
- **c.** Cumbria
- **d.** Warwickshire

3 Which cereal crop is grown in paddy fields?
- **a.** Amarant
- **b.** Maize
- **c.** Rice
- **d.** Millet

4 What name is given to the hard grains left after the milling of flour, used in milk puddings and in pasta?
- **a.** Semolina
- **b.** Sago
- **c.** Cornmeal
- **d.** Tapioca

5 To which crop is the Colorado beetle a serious pest?
- **a.** Carrot
- **b.** Tomato
- **c.** Wheat
- **d.** Potato

6 Pomology is the branch of botany that studies and cultivates what?
- **a.** Vegetables
- **b.** Herbs
- **c.** Fruits
- **d.** Ferns

7 What type of creature is the Hawaiian honeycreeper?
- **a.** A lizard
- **b.** A bird
- **c.** A bee
- **d.** A wasp

8 What does a dendrophobiac fear?
- **a.** Birds
- **b.** Fish
- **c.** Flowers
- **d.** Trees

Each leaf contains either a true statement or a false statement, and your task is to begin at the one marked 'START', following a continuous line, travelling from leaf to touching leaf, until you reach the one marked 'END'. Every true statement is used in the path from 'START' to 'END', so there are no shortcuts, no paths may cross, nor can any leaf be used twice in order to reach your destination!

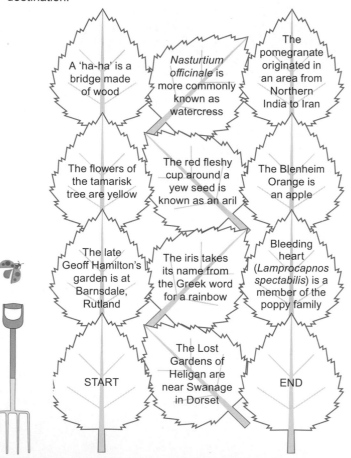

A 'ha-ha' is a bridge made of wood

Nasturtium officinale is more commonly known as watercress

The pomegranate originated in an area from Northern India to Iran

The flowers of the tamarisk tree are yellow

The red fleshy cup around a yew seed is known as an aril

The Blenheim Orange is an apple

The late Geoff Hamilton's garden is at Barnsdale, Rutland

The iris takes its name from the Greek word for a rainbow

Bleeding heart (*Lamprocapnos spectabilis*) is a member of the poppy family

START

The Lost Gardens of Heligan are near Swanage in Dorset

END

See how many of the questions below you can correctly answer.

1   What is the national tree of Lebanon (it is displayed on the Lebanese flag and coat of arms)?

2   What type of tree is the sweet bay?

3   From which tree is gum arabic obtained?

4   What is another name for the Canary whitewood or American whitewood?

5   To which genus do cherry and plum trees belong?

6   Which 'greenhouse' gas is absorbed by trees?

7   Which Australian tree is also called a gum tree?

8   Which genus of trees and shrubs includes the holly?

9   What substance obtained from the sapodilla tree is used to make chewing gum?

10   What are *Moringa oleifera* trees better known as (from the taste of the roots, which resembles a certain condiment)?

11   Which tree's Latin name is *Juglans regia*?

Quotation

An optimistic gardener is one who believes that whatever goes down must come up.

Leslie Hall

49 Birds

See how many of the questions below you can correctly answer.

1 A frequent visitor to bird tables, by what common name do we know the gregarious bird *Sturnus vulgaris*?

2 To which family of birds do canaries and siskins belong?

3 What name is given to the vocal organ of birds?

4 What type of bird is a gadwall?

5 Which bird has 'song', 'mistle' and 'hermit' varieties?

6 Which bird of the crow family has the Latin name *Pica pica*?

7 Which bird of the family *Picidae* punches through tree bark with its long straight bill in search of insects?

8 Which bird with a very distinctive call lays its eggs in the nests of other birds?

9 Which of these birds (if any) can fly: cassowary, emu, kiwi, kookaburra, ostrich, rhea?

10 Which bird has 'ring-necked', 'golden' and 'argus' varieties?

11 To which family of birds does the bittern belong?

Quotation

The garden suggests there might be a place where we can meet nature halfway.

Michael Pollan

Match the silhouettes of these flowers to their names in the list below.

ASTILBE	LUPIN
IRIS	NARCISSUS
LOVE-LIES-BLEEDING	NICOTIANA

Place the letters of each word, one per cell, so that every word flows in a clockwise direction around a number.

Where the hexagons of one word overlap with those of another, the letter in each cell is common to both.

When finished, rearrange the letters in the pale green hexagons to form the name of a salad vegetable.

AWHILE

BEHELD

BELFRY

CURFEW

FOSTER

HEREBY

KETTLE

SECRET

STRUCK

THWART

WEEKLY

O

3 2 1

4

E

5 6 7

T

8

11 10 9

C

Answer: _____

See how many of the questions below you can correctly answer.

1 With which architect, whose most famous creation is possibly the Cenotaph in London, did Gertrude Jekyll have a long professional association?

2 Jekyll designed several large gardens in the USA, the most famous being Glebe House, Woodbury: in which New England state?

3 Which 19th century art movement most influenced Jekyll in terms of colour?

4 In which English county is Hestercombe House, the gardens of which were completed to Jekyll's designs in 1906?

5 Jekyll designed the walled garden of which Northumberland castle, the site of an earlier priory that was attacked by Vikings during the 8th and 9th centuries?

6 To further develop her interests in botany and art, at the age of 18 Jekyll enrolled at which London school in 1861?

7 For which magazine, launched in 1897 and still going strong today, did Jekyll contribute many articles?

8 Jekyll designed the surrounding gardens for a five-foot tall dolls' house, on display at Windsor Castle. For which royal person was the doll's house completed in 1924?

9 The Victoria Medal of Honour was awarded to Jekyll by which society in 1897?

10 Her last home, Munstead Wood, close to where Jekyll spent most of her childhood, is located on the outskirts of which Surrey town?

See how many of the questions below you can correctly answer.

1 What name is given to a broom made of twigs tied round a stick?

2 Often seen growing on rocks and old walls, what name is given to organisms comprising an alga and a fungus in a symbiotic association?

3 Of what is bryology the study?

4 What word describes the scientific study of the physiology, structure, genetics, ecology, distribution, classification, and economic importance of plants?

5 Which tough-stemmed Eurasian plant that typically has purple thistle-like flower heads is also known as 'hardhead'?

6 Which plant has 'bird's-foot' and 'hop' varieties?

7 Which gigantic tropical and subtropical grass has hollow, jointed woody stems and edible young shoots?

8 What is a loquat?

9 What is the common English name for the genus *Papaver*?

10 What word describes a plant having stamens and pistils in the same flower?

Quotation

If I finish my day with no garden dirt under my fingernails and nothing new learned, it is a day wasted.

Valerie Clague

54 Wordladder

Change one letter at a time (but not the position of any letter) to make a new word – and move from the word at the top of the ladder to the word at the bottom using the exact number of rungs provided.

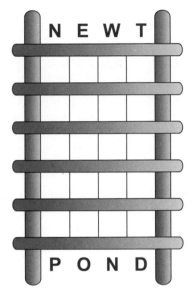

N E W T

P O N D

55 True or False

Can you decide whether the statement below is true or false?

Saffron is an orange-yellow flavouring, food colouring, and dye made from the dried stigmas of the crocus.

True or **False**

56 Whatever the Weather...

See how many of the questions below you can correctly answer.

1 What term describes the degree of moisture present in the air?

2 "If on St Swithin's it do rain, for forty days shall it remain" is an old saying – on which date is St Swithin's Day?

3 What is the name of the hot dry wind which blows from the Sahara, across the Mediterranean and into Europe?

4 Which are the highest type of clouds: stratocumulus, altostratus or cirrus?

5 What is the name for the circulation of water from the atmosphere through the land and rivers, into the oceans and back into the atmosphere?

6 Which dark grey clouds are commonly called rain clouds?

7 Which part of Britain is the warmest, with an average annual temperature of 11.8 degrees Celsius?

8 In a rainbow, what colour comes between orange and green?

9 On 10 August 2003, where in England did the temperature for the first time exceed 100 degrees Fahrenheit, the hottest recorded in the UK?

10 What plant is also known as 'poor man's weatherglass', because it has flowers that close in cloudy or rainy weather?

Quotation

If you build up the soil with organic material, the plants will do just fine.

John Harrison

54

Petal Puzzle

How many words of three or more letters can you make from those on the petals, without using plurals, abbreviations or proper nouns? The central letter must appear once in every word and no letter may be used more than once unless it is on a different petal. There is at least one nine-letter word to be found.

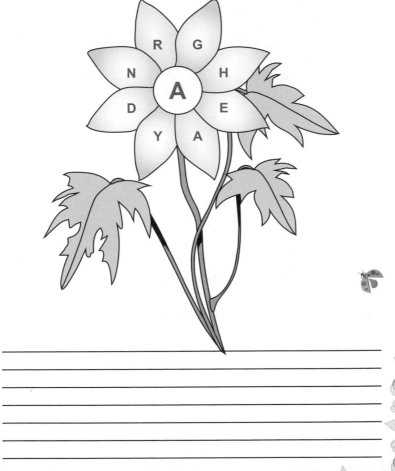

_____

_____

_____

_____

_____

_____

58 Food and Drink

See how many of the questions below you can correctly answer.

1 The pods of which plant are used to thicken the spicy soup known as gumbo?

2 What name is given to the Russian soup made with beetroot and usually served with sour cream?

3 'Parmentier' is a term given to a dish made with or accompanied by which vegetables?

4 What is used to flavour Pernod, pastis and ouzo?

5 Haggis is traditionally served with which two vegetables, called 'neeps' and 'tatties'?

6 Which spice is used to flavour goulash, a traditional Hungarian stew of meat and vegetables?

7 What culinary word is used to describe vegetables cut into thin strips and usually served in soup or as a garnish?

8 Which fruit gives a distinctive flavour to slivovitz, a brandy made chiefly in Romania, Serbia and neighbouring states?

9 What is the name for the selection of hot and cold hors d'oeuvres of meat and vegetables served in Eastern Mediterranean and Middle Eastern countries?

10 Which two vegetables are the main ingredients of 'bubble and squeak'?

Quotation

There is no gardening without humility. Nature is constantly sending even its oldest scholars to the bottom of the class for some egregious blunder.

Alfred Austin

59 Garden Borders

Fit the letters G, A, R, D, E and N into the grid in such a way that each horizontal row, each vertical column and each of the heavily bordered sections of six squares contains a different letter. Some letters are already in place.

R		A			
				G	D
			E		N
E				D	G
	R				A

60 Vegetable Tracker

Starting at the top left corner and ending at the bottom right, track a path from letter to letter, in any direction except diagonally, in order to find the hidden vegetables. All of the letters must be used once only.

L	E	T	T	U	I	F	W	E	R	O	C	C	P	I	N	A
R	R	E	S	C	L	L	O	R	B	O	P	O	S	O	H	C
O	A	M	E	E	U	S	O	T	A	T	I	L	P	N	I	O
W	T	U	R	C	A	A	L	S	I	F	Y	N	I	A	C	N
C	P	R	B	A	L	A	C	I	R	E	C	S	R	B	K	A
A	I	N	A	R	C	H	C	A	E	L	I	S	A	B	E	L
R	R	O	T	T	I	O	K	E	R	A	D	H	P	A	G	E

61 Spot the Same

Which two scarecrows are identical in every detail?

62 Spelling Bee

Which is the only one of the following to be correctly spelled?

a   PELERGONIUM

b   PELORGONIAM

c   PELARGONIUM

d   PELORGONIUM

63 The Natural World

Find the correct answer to each question from the four alternatives.

1 Important to the caviar industry of Russia, what kind of fish is a beluga?
    a. Catfish   **b.** Trout
    c. Sturgeon   **d.** Salmon

2 Crabs and lobsters are just two members of the decapod order of animals. What does 'decapod' mean?
    a. Has eight legs   **b.** Has ten legs
    c. Has a shell   **d.** Has claws

3 Which is the only mammal to have finned feet and tusks?
    a. Sea lion   **b.** Elephant seal
    c. Narwhal   **d.** Walrus

4 The aurochs, a native European animal rendered extinct in the early 17th century, was what kind of animal?
    a. Giant deer   **b.** Wild ox
    c. Mountain goat   **d.** Large boar

5 What is the name of the long, venomous tree-dwelling snake (*Dispholidus typus*) of southern Africa?
    a. Aardslang   **b.** Black mamba
    c. Great asp   **d.** Boomslang

6 The lemming, a small rodent, is found only in which region?
    a. Tasmania   **b.** The Sahara Desert
    c. The Arctic   **d.** Japan

7 The Australian kookaburra is a member of which family of birds?
    a. Kingfisher   **b.** Crow
    c. Parrot   **d.** Starling

64 General Knowledge

See how many of the questions below you can correctly answer.

1 What colour are the berries of the cuckoo pint (*Arum maculatum*)?

2 What is the common name of the late-flowering perennial garden plant of the genus *Solidago* that has long-pointed, lance-shaped leaves and numerous deep yellow-shaded flower heads in a pyramid-shaped pinnacle?

3 Where on a mushroom is the 'umbo' to be found?

4 What is another name for digitalis?

5 Which plant is associated with Ireland and, in particular, St Patrick's Day?

6 What name is more commonly given to the biennial plant *Brassica rapa*?

7 What is sorghum?

8 What sort of creature is a nuthatch?

9 What word describes the pruning of shrubs and trees into ornamental shapes?

Quotation

Working with plants, trees, fences and walls, if they practise sincerely they will attain enlightenment.

Dogen Zenji

65 Garden Maze

How successful will you be in trying to find a route to the centre of this garden maze?

66 Salad Sudoku

Every row, every column and each of the nine smaller boxes of nine squares should be filled with a different number from 1 to 9 inclusive. Some numbers are already in place. When the grid is completely filled, decode the numbers in the shaded squares, then rearrange the letters to spell out the name of a salad vegetable or fruit.

	5				1	9	4	
			7					3
						5		8
8				9		7		
9	2		8		7		5	1
		3		2				9
5		4						
3					5			
	1	2	9				6	

Code

1	2	3	4	5	6	7	8	9
E	G	I	N	O	P	R	S	T

Answer: _____

See how many of the questions below you can correctly answer.

1 How is the house plant *Chlorophytum elatum* better known?

2 What is a tonka?

3 *Calluna*, *Daboecia* and *Erica* are three genera of which small evergreen shrub?

4 Before pumpkins became readily available in the UK, which vegetables were hollowed out and carved with faces to make Halloween lanterns?

5 Which conservation charity was founded in 1972 by Kenneth Watkins and has its headquarters in Grantham, Lincolnshire?

6 What term describes the cutting off of the top and branches of a tree to encourage new growth?

7 What sort of creature is a loon?

8 What name is given to a pair of pruning clippers with crossed blades, for use with one hand?

9 What word describes a layer of material such as compost, leaf mould or bark chippings spread over the surface of the soil to suppress weeds and conserve moisture?

10 'Bryanston', 'Golden Transparent' and 'Ingall's Grimoldby' are all varieties of which type of plum?

Quotation

We know more about the movement of celestial bodies than about the soil underfoot.

Leonardo da Vinci

68 Parks and Gardens

See how many of the questions below you can correctly answer.

1 In which county is Tatton Park, one of the Royal Horticultural Society's recommended gardens?

2 The first botanical garden in the United States, Bartram's Garden, was founded in 1730 in which US state?

3 Which gardens, made famous on television, consist of 38 different gardens, including 'Gentleman's Cottage Garden', 'Artisan's Cottage Garden' and 'The Lands' End Garden'?

4 Which national park lies virtually in the middle of mainland Scotland?

5 Which pinetum was established as the National Conifer Collection in 1925 and is now recognised as having the most complete collection of conifers on one site anywhere in the world?

6 Which poetically-named tree (*Ailanthus altissima*) is common in parks and squares in London and was introduced from China in the 18th century? It acquired its name from its ability to rapidly grow tall.

7 Founded in 1545, which is the world's oldest academic botanical garden still in its original location?

8 Which garden in Chelsea was opened to the public for the first time in 1983?

9 Which US national park lies in the Sierra Nevada and is famous for its giant sequoia trees?

Quotation

It will never rain roses: when we want to have more roses we must plant more trees.

George Eliot

69 Shape-up

Every row and column in this grid originally contained one bird, one flower, one leaf, one mushroom and two blank squares, although not necessarily in that order. Every symbol with a black arrow refers to the first of the four symbols encountered in the direction of the arrow. Every symbol with a white arrow refers to the second of the four symbols encountered in the direction of the arrow. Can you complete the original grid?

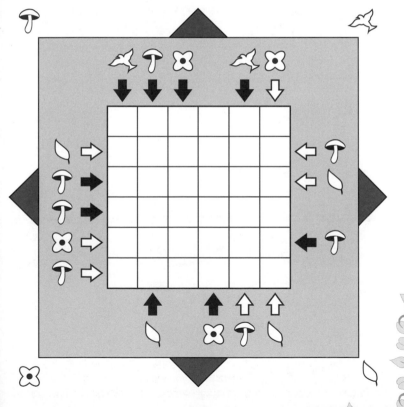

70 What's It Worth?

Each symbol stands for a different number. In order to reach the correct total at the end of each row and column, what is the value of the bird, flower, leaf and mushroom?

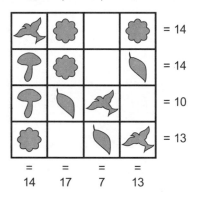

71 Shape Spotter

Which is the only shape to appear twice in exactly the same shading (black, white or green) in the box below? You'll need a keen eye for this one, as some shapes overlap others!

72) Plants in Music

See how many of the questions below you can correctly answer.

1 Which song with 'flowers' in the title was a hit for Barbra Streisand and Neil Diamond in 1978?

2 *Jennifer Juniper* was a 1968 hit for which folk-rock singer?

3 Which Beatles song appeared on a double A-side single with *Strawberry Fields Forever*?

4 Who wrote the music for the opera *Der Rosenkavalier* (*The Knight of the Rose*)?

5 Who sang the most famous version of *Day-O (The Banana Boat Song)*?

6 *On the Trail of the Lonesome Pine* was a song appearing in the 1937 film *Way Out West*, featuring which comedy duo?

7 *Love Grows (Where My Rosemary Goes)* was a one-hit wonder for which band in 1970?

8 The 'Windflower' motif is a recurring theme in the violin concerto by which English composer?

9 Together with fellow singers Ritchie Valens and J P Richardson, which American singer died in an aircraft crash in February 1959?

10 *O Tannenbaum* is the title of a traditional German Christmas carol. What is the English translation of the German word 'tannenbaum'?

11 Who sang *I'll Pick a Rose for My Rose*, a UK top ten hit back in 1969?

See how many of the questions below you can correctly answer.

1 Which North American shrub (*Symphoricarpos albus*) of the honeysuckle family, bears white berries and is often cultivated as an ornamental or for hedging?

2 What method of propagation involves the splitting of clumps of plants either by hand, or by using a knife, or by levering with two forks placed back-to-back?

3 Bearing long spikes of flowers, by what name is the plant Kniphofia (of the former genus *Tritoma*) better known?

4 In botany, what name is given to the vascular tissue in plants that conducts sugars and other metabolic products downwards from the leaves…?

5 …and what name is given to the tissue that conducts water and dissolved nutrients upwards from the root?

6 What type of creature was 'Brian' in BBC TV's children's programme *The Magic Roundabout*?

7 What sort of creature (of the genus *Gavia*) is a loon?

8 Grown for their showy flowers, commonly blue and purple, but also white and pink, *Agapanthus* are also called what?

9 Kett's oak traditionally represents the place where the Wymondham and Hethersett rebels met before marching (in protest at the enclosure of land) in July 1549, to which county town?

Quotation

If a tree dies, plant another in its place.

Carolus Linnaeus

74 Trailing Vine

The object of this puzzle is to trace a single path from the top left square to the bottom right square of the grid, moving through all of the cells in either a horizontal, vertical or diagonal direction. Every cell must be entered once only and your path should take you through the letters in the sequence V-I-N-E-V-I-N-E, etc. Can you find the logical way through?

V	I	V	I	E	V	E	V
V	N	E	N	N	I	N	I
I	E	V	I	V	N	V	N
V	N	N	E	I	E	I	E
I	E	I	E	N	E	I	N
V	N	V	N	E	V	V	E
I	E	V	I	V	N	I	N
N	E	I	N	E	V	I	E

General Knowledge

See how many of the questions below you can correctly answer.

1 'Golden Tiara', 'Halcyon' and 'Sum and Substance' are all varieties of which popular and fully hardy foliage plant?

2 The site of the annual Masters Tournament, which golf club in the USA was formerly a plant nursery, and has each hole on the course named after a tree or shrub?

3 The timber of which tree was formerly used to make longbows?

4 What type of creature is a firefly, the winged male and flightless female of which both have luminescent organs?

5 Which small brown bird is also called a hedge sparrow?

6 What colour features prominently on the forewings of the males of the butterfly *Anthocharis cardamines*, giving rise to the name by which they are commonly known?

7 A flower described as 'campanulate' has what shape?

8 What name is given to the aquatic larvae of frogs and toads?

9 What name is given to flowerless plants with feathery or leafy fronds, that reproduce by spores released from the undersides of the fronds?

Quotation

When you have done your best for a flower, and it fails, you have some reason to be aggrieved.

Frank Swinnerton

76 Riddle-Me-Ree

Find one letter per line, following the clues given in the verse below. For example, 'My first is in houses, but never in homes' gives the letter U as the first letter. When you have finished, the letters will spell another word.

My first is in ROSE, and also in STOCK,

My second's in LOAM, but not seen in ROCK,

My third's not in LEMON, but is found in LIME,

My fourth Is in LOVAGE, but never in THYME,

My fifth's not in PARSNIP, although it's in PEA,

My whole is a fruit that grows on a tree.

1st	2nd	3rd	4th	5th

77 True or False

Can you decide whether the statement below is true or false?

Mycology is the scientific study of mosses and liverworts.

True or **False**

Telephone Code

Use the telephone dial in order to spell out a quotation attributed to George Cadbury.

1 9 8   4 3   3 1 2 4   5 1 6   2 6 9 5 2   4 1 9 3   4 4 8   6 9 6

4 6 9 8 3 ,   1   5 1 7 3 3   3 1 7 2 3 6   8 6   2 9 5 8 4 9 1 8 3

1 6 2   4 3 1 5 8 4 0   8 9 7 7 6 9 6 2 4 6 3 8 – 8 4 3 6 ,

4   8 4 6 9 3 4 8 ,   8 4 3 7 3   9 4 5 5   1 3   3 6 7   8 4 3 5

1   1 3 8 8 3 7   6 6 6 6 7 8 9 6 4 8 0   6 3   1   4 1 6 6 0

3 1 5 4 5 0   5 4 3 3 .

Find the correct answer to each question from the four alternatives.

1 How many eyes have most spiders?
   a. Ten   **b.** Six
   c. Four   **d.** Eight

2 What is Britain's smallest native bird?
   a. Wren   **b.** Dunnock
   c. Blue tit   **d.** Goldcrest

3 What is the name for a young eel?
   a. Eelet   **b.** Elver
   c. Slender   **d.** Sprat

4 Which is the largest of the whales?
   a. Balleen whale   **b.** Sperm whale
   c. Blue whale   **d.** Humpback whale

5 Although present in their billions up until the 18th century, which North American bird was rendered extinct, the last having died in the Cincinnati Zoological Garden in September 1914?
   a. Grey dove   **b.** Atlantic crow
   c. Passenger pigeon   **d.** Columbus sparrow

6 The duck-billed platypus and the echidna (of which there are four species) are the only mammals to do what?
   a. Lay eggs   **b.** Live entirely in water
   c. Nest in trees   **d.** Live in river bed nests

7 Which Australian animal comes in two basic types: the bare-nosed (or common) and the hairy-nosed?
   a. Koala   **b.** Wombat
   c. Kangaroo   **d.** Dingo

See how many of the questions below you can correctly answer.

1 Which beautiful youth rejected the nymph Echo and fell in love with his own reflection in a pool, pining away and changing into the flower that bears his name?

2 What was the name given to the Tree of Life, or World Tree, of Norse mythology?

3 Known in Hindu mythology as 'the wish-fulfilling tree', which tree (*Ficus benghalensis*) represents eternal life?

4 In Greek mythology, Adonis died after being wounded by a wild boar, leading to the origin of the red form of which flower that grew from each drop of blood that fell?

5 What is the birth flower for people born in the month of November?

6 Identified by the Romans with Ceres, who was the Greek goddess of agriculture and corn?

7 Which plant (*Allium sativum*) was once used to ward off vampires: it could be worn, hung in windows, or rubbed on chimneys and keyholes?

8 Which plant yields a fruit represented by Homer as producing in those who ate it a state of dreamy forgetfulness and loss of all desire to return home?

9 Which plant was named after the Greek hero who died after he was struck by a discus as it fell to the ground?

Quotation

There can be no other occupation like gardening in which, if you were to creep up behind someone at their work, you would find them smiling.

Mirabel Osler

Spidoku

Each of the eight segments of the spider's web should be filled with a different number from 1 to 8, in such a way that every ring also contains a different number from 1 to 8. The segments run from the outside of the spider's web to the centre, and the rings run all the way around.

Some numbers are already in place. Can you fill in the rest?

Latin List

Pair up each of the numbered boxes on the left with the lettered boxes on the right to match the common names of plants with their botanical (or 'Latin') names.

| 1 | Blackthorn |

| a | *Vinca* |

| 2 | Catmint |

| b | *Erysimum* |

| 3 | Lilac |

| c | *Lonicera* |

| 4 | Periwinkle |

| d | *Salvia officinalis* |

| 5 | Honeysuckle |

| e | *Nepeta* |

| 6 | Sage |

| f | *Syringa* |

| 7 | Wallflower |

| g | *Muscari* |

| 8 | Grape hyacinth |

| h | *Prunus spinosa* |

Number	Letter
1	
2	
3	
4	

Number	Letter
5	
6	
7	
8	

See how many of the questions below you can correctly answer.

1 Which TV gardener (and his wife) wrote *The Jewel Garden*?

2 Which makeover show starred Diarmuid Gavin, Anne McKevitt, Tessa Shaw and Kevin McCloud?

3 On air since 1947, and originally called *How Does your Garden Grow?*, which radio programme features a panel of the best brains in horticulture…?

4 …and by which radio station is it broadcast?

5 Which 2005-6 television series introduced by David Attenborough looked at the lives and environments of invertebrates?

6 Who first appeared on *Gardener's World* in 1998 when Geoff Hamilton did a feature on her garden, Glebe Cottage in north Devon?

7 Hosted by Alan Titchmarsh, which programme was first broadcast on ITV on 10 June 2011?

8 Which much-loved BBC Scotland programme was first broadcast on 14 April 1978?

9 Who presented *The A to Z of TV Gardening*, getting inspiration and advice from some of the BBC's most popular gardening presenters and programmes?

10 Who is billed as 'a genuine, 21st-century tree-hugger' and hosts the Channel 4 series *The City Gardener*?

11 Who presented such programmes as *The Joy of Gardening* and appeared as a gardening expert on ITV's *Daybreak* breakfast magazine show?

Find the correct answer to each question from the four alternatives.

1 The amethyst deceiver, a small purple toadstool, is found in which habitat?
a. Grassland   **b.** Coastal
c. Heathland   **d.** Woodland

2 Rarely seen outside of East Anglia, to which genus of plants does the oxlip belong?
a. *Ranunculus*   **b.** *Primula*
c. *Bellis*   **d.** *Stachys*

3 Which one of the following is not a bat?
a. Muscardine   **b.** Barbastelle
c. Serotine   **d.** Pipistrelle

4 Following fertilisation, what part of a flower becomes a fruit?
a. Style   **b.** Anther
c. Stigma   **d.** Ovary

5 What is the *Fagus sylvatica* tree?
a. Elm   **b.** Lime
c. Beech   **d.** Ash

6 Which part of a tree is used to make cork?
a. Root   **b.** Bark
c. Crown   **d.** Sap

7 What does a pteridologist study?
a. Birds   **b.** Ferns
c. Bromeliads   **d.** Parasitic plants

8 To which order of insects do ants, wasps and bees belong?
a. Siphunculata   **b.** Diplura
c. Ephemeroptera   **d.** Hymenoptera

85 Round the Block

You won't need a starting block to get you under way, because it isn't a race! Just arrange the six-letter solutions to the clues into the six blocks around each clue number. Write the answers in a clockwise or anticlockwise direction and you'll find that the last answer fits into the first; the main problem will be to decide in which square to put the first letter of each word…

When read in a clockwise direction (not necessarily starting at either of the topmost squares), the letters in the pale green squares spell out the name of a bird you might see in the garden.

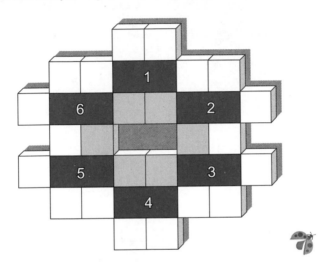

1 Severe shortage of food

2 Shackle for the ankles or feet

3 Glass container for liquids such as water, beer, etc

4 Submissive to training or direction

5 Place where films are shown

6 Ball game associated with Wimbledon

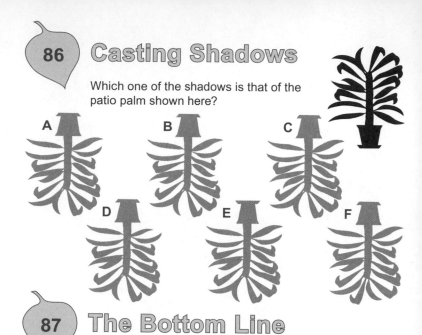

86 Casting Shadows

Which one of the shadows is that of the patio palm shown here?

A B C

D E F

87 The Bottom Line

The bottom line of this grid is waiting to be filled. Every square in the solution contains only one symbol from rows 1 to 5 above, although two or more squares in the solution may contain the same symbol. At the end of every numbered row is a score, which shows:

1 the number of symbols placed in the correct finishing position on the bottom line, as indicated by a tick; and

2 the number of symbols which appear on the bottom line, but in a different position, as indicated by a cross.

Can you fill each square with the correct symbol?

					Score
1					X X X
2					✓ X
3					X X
4					X X
5					X
					✓✓✓✓

Poet's Corner

Find the correct answer to each question from the four alternatives.

1 "An English unofficial rose". To which flower was Rupert Brooke referring in his poem *The Old Vicarage, Grantchester*?

2 "Of man's first disobedience, and the fruit of that forbidden tree..." is the opening of which poem by John Milton?

3 "A fool sees not the same tree that a wise man sees." Which poet wrote these words in *Proverbs of Hell*?

4 Who did Alfred Tennyson coax into the garden where "the woodbine spices are wafted abroad, and the musk of the roses blown"?

5 "I think that I shall never see, a poem lovely as a tree" begins the poem *Trees*, written by whom?

6 "O chestnut tree, great rooted blossomer, Are you the leaf, the blossom or the bole?" are two lines from which poem written by William Butler Yeats?

7 In his poem *To the Daisy*, who described the daisy as "the poet's darling"?

8 "The curfew tolls the knell of parting day..." is the first line of which poem by Thomas Gray?

Quotation

Everything that slows us down and forces patience, everything that sets us back into the slow circles of nature, is a help. Gardening is an instrument of grace.

May Sarton

See how many of the questions below you can correctly answer.

1 Attempting to represent plants as different levels within the British social class structure, what is the title of the second chapter of Lewis Carroll's sequel to *Alice in Wonderland*, *Through the Looking Glass*?

2 Who wrote *Around the World in 80 Gardens* and *The Ivington Diaries*?

3 Which children's book opens with "The Mole had been working very hard all the morning, spring cleaning his little home"?

4 Which fictional country estate is owned by Fitzwilliam Darcy, the male protagonist in Jane Austen's novel *Pride and Prejudice?*

5 Which short story by Oscar Wilde tells of a giant who builds a wall to keep children out of his beautiful garden?

6 A famous medieval garden features in which French allegory, where the narrator tries to gain access to his loved one, symbolised by a rose being kept in a "Garden of Love"?

7 Who wrote the short story *Kew Gardens*, observing four couples and a snail at Kew in summer as they move past a flower bed?

8 Sir Percy Blakeney is the title character in which play and adventure novel by Emma Orczy set during the Reign of Terror following the start of the French Revolution?

9 Who wrote *The Wild Garden* and *The English Flower Garden* and, in 1884, purchased the Elizabethan manor of Gravetye near East Grinstead in Sussex?

Quotation

The garden, by design, is concerned with both the interior and the land beyond the garden.

Stephen Gardiner

In Code

Each letter in the names of these plants is represented by a number which remains the same for that letter wherever it occurs on the page. Work out the code to reveal the common names of the plants. Some numbers are already decoded.

1	2	3	3	2	4
Z					

5	6	7	3	8	9

10	7	4	3

11	12	13	3	14	4	2	3

4	15	9

16	12	3	17	12	3
			D		

18	6	2	17	7

19	4	2	16	16	4	6	17	2	4
					A				

9	20	18	7	6	2	8	13	11
	Y							

10	12	13	19	4	2	3	21	2	16	16	7	4
		G										

7	13	8	4	16	20	18	14	13	15
									S

91 Daffodil Dilemma

Ivor Dibber has been given a plan by his wife, who would like some daffodil bulbs to be planted in a square patch of grass. Mrs Dibber has made a grid map, showing the long-suffering Ivor exactly where the bulbs are to be planted, and she has decided to test Ivor's brain (and patience) by making a puzzle of it…

Those squares containing numbers are empty, but where a number appears in a square, it indicates how many daffodil bulbs are to be planted in the squares (up to a maximum of eight) surrounding the numbered one, touching it at any corner or side. There is only one bulb in any individual square.

Ivor needs your help. Place a circle into every square that should contain a daffodil bulb.

		1		2	1	2			0
	3	1	2						1
					3		1		
	2		3		4		2		1
0		1		3					0
1			1	2			4		
2							4		0
			2						2
		3			4		5		
	0			3				2	2

92 The Natural World

Find the correct answer to each question from the four alternatives.

1 Which is the world's longest continental mountain range?
- **a.** Karakorum
- **b.** Himalayas
- **c.** Rocky Mountains
- **d.** Andes

2 On Boxing Day of which year did the Indian Ocean earthquake and tsunami take place?
- **a.** 2005
- **b.** 2004
- **c.** 2006
- **d.** 2003

3 Sirocco, foehn, mistral and chinook are all types of what phenomena?
- **a.** Winds
- **b.** Ocean warm currents
- **c.** Clouds
- **d.** Ocean cold currents

4 Cape Agulhas is the southernmost point of which continent?
- **a.** South America
- **b.** Europe
- **c.** Australia
- **d.** Africa

5 What kind of animal is a basilisk?
- **a.** Bird
- **b.** Turtle
- **c.** Lizard
- **d.** Fish

6 Which species of fish is the world's most venomous?
- **a.** Stonefish
- **b.** Angler fish
- **c.** Barracuda
- **d.** Piranha

7 What is the name for a young hare?
- **a.** Leveret
- **b.** Pup
- **c.** Buck
- **d.** Heveret

8 Which bird was regarded as sacred by the Ancient Egyptians?
- **a.** Turtle dove
- **b.** Desert eagle
- **c.** Pheasant
- **d.** Ibis

True or False Maze

Each leaf contains either a true statement or a false statement, and your task is to begin at the one marked 'START', following a continuous line, travelling from leaf to touching leaf, until you reach the one marked 'END'. Every true statement is used in the path from 'START' to 'END', so there are no shortcuts, no paths may cross, nor can any leaf be used twice in order to reach your destination!

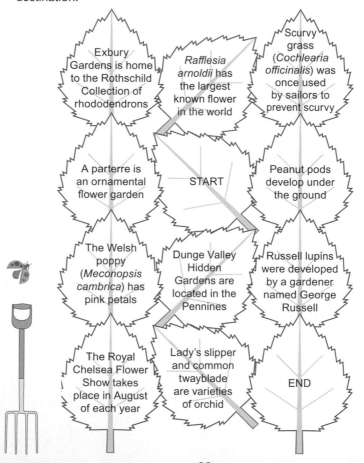

Exbury Gardens is home to the Rothschild Collection of rhododendrons

Rafflesia arnoldii has the largest known flower in the world

Scurvy grass (*Cochlearia officinalis*) was once used by sailors to prevent scurvy

A parterre is an ornamental flower garden

START

Peanut pods develop under the ground

The Welsh poppy (*Meconopsis cambrica*) has pink petals

Dunge Valley Hidden Gardens are located in the Pennines

Russell lupins were developed by a gardener named George Russell

The Royal Chelsea Flower Show takes place in August of each year

Lady's slipper and common twayblade are varieties of orchid

END

See how many of the questions below you can correctly answer.

1 Of which fruit is the shaddock a variety?

2 Which tall umbellifer, *Anthriscus sylvestris*, with white flowers and finely cut leaves, is also known as Queen Anne's lace?

3 Which plant was named after Adam Lonicer, a German botanist and professor of mathematics?

4 The common name of which plant comes from a 16th century Italian marquess who invented a plumeria-scented perfume?

5 What powered tool, popular with vegetable gardeners, was invented by Arthur Clifford Howard in 1912?

6 What type of tree is the 'Joshua tree', so named because the plant was likened to Joshua brandishing a spear?

7 With leaves of up to three metres in diameter, what type of plant is *Victoria amazonica*?

8 Inspired by an invention of Christopher Cockerell's, what aid to gardening was invented by Karl Dahlman in the 1960s?

9 What word describes a spike of flowers closely arranged round a fleshy axis and typically enclosed in a spathe, characteristic of the arums?

Quotation

There are two seasonal diversions that can ease the bite of any winter. One is the January thaw. The other is the seed catalogues.

Hal Borland

95 Who Said What?

See how many of the questions below you can correctly answer.

1 Who said: "A cucumber should be well-sliced and dressed with pepper and vinegar then thrown out as good for nothing."?

2 Who said: "Keep your love of nature, for that is the true way to understand art more and more."?

3 According to Mark Twain, which vegetable was "nothing but a cabbage with a college education."?

4 Who said: "There is a tendency in nature to the continued progression of certain classes of varieties further and further from the original type."?

5 Former US president George Bush Snr once publicly stated that he totally disliked which vegetable?

6 Who said: "I am quite conscious that my speculations run quite beyond the bounds of true science."?

7 "Everything is the product of one universal creative effort. There is nothing dead in Nature." This is a quote attributed to which Roman philosopher?

8 Who said: "In nature, there is less death and destruction than death and transmutation."?

9 Which French sculptor of bronze and marble figures said: "To the artist there is never anything ugly in nature."?

10 Who said: "Nature is my manifestation of God. I go to nature every day for inspiration in the day's work. I follow in building the principles which nature has used in its domain."?

Match the silhouettes of these trees to their names in the list below.

1

2

3

4

5

6

BIRCH   PINE

MAPLE   POPLAR

OAK   SPRUCE

Place the letters of each word, one per cell, so that every word flows in a clockwise direction around a number.

Where the hexagons of one word overlap with those of another, the letter in each cell is common to both.

When finished, rearrange the letters in the pale green hexagons to form the name of a tree.

BYLINE

CLIMAX

COFFEE

DEJECT

DRUDGE

DULCET

ENTICE

EYEFUL

HOMILY

RITUAL

YEARLY

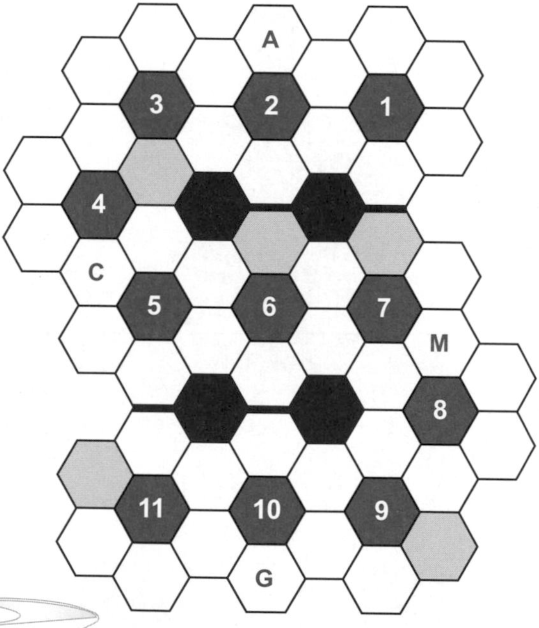

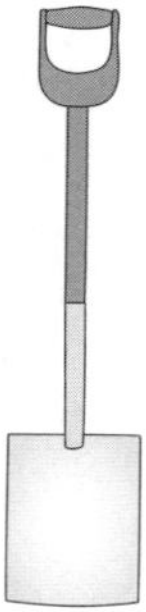

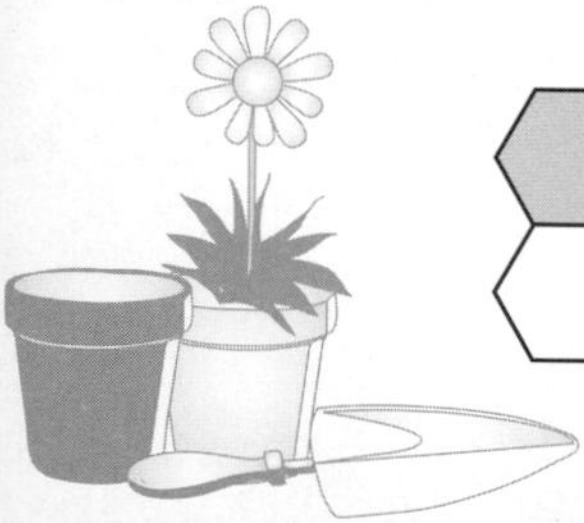

Answer: _____

98 Vita Sackville-West

See how many of the questions below you can correctly answer.

1 Known as 'Vita' all her life, what was Sackville-West's real first given name?

2 In 1930, which ruined castle in Kent did Vita and her husband buy and commence to refurbish, creating the famous garden that survives today?

3 Although today she is perhaps best known for her landscaping work, what were Vita's two more important occupations during her lifetime?

4 With which famous female writer (a member of the Bloomsbury Group) did Vita have an affair?

5 Which Kent manor house and park was Vita's childhood home?

6 One of Vita's essential design ideas involved the use of plants of one predominant colour: which?

7 Her designs often took in natural or existing structures to create defined areas in a garden. How did these defined areas come to be known?

8 In 1947 Vita started to write a weekly column entitled *In Your Garden*: for which UK newspaper?

9 Which writer and guest presenter of BBC TV's *Gardener's World* has authored a book entitled *Vita Sackville West's Sissinghurst: The Creation of a Garden* based on Vita's work at Sissinghurst?

10 Vita Sackville-West died in June of which year?

99 General Knowledge

See how many of the questions below you can correctly answer.

1 The small white or yellow caterpillars with black heads that tunnel their way into the flesh of apples are the larvae of which moth (*Cydia pomonella*)?

2 By what more common name do we know the fragrant plant *Matthiola longipetala*?

3 'Early Rivers', 'Colney' and 'Kordia' are all varieties of which fruit?

4 The EMR's work on perennial fruit crops is known internationally: what do the letters EMR stand for?

5 Which group of plants has 'blue-green', 'yellow-green' and 'golden-brown' varieties?

6 What is a pond-skater?

7 What is the common name of the bird *Troglodytes troglodytes*?

8 What sort of creature is a devil's coach-horse?

9 A pupil and successor of Aristotle, which Greek philosopher and scientist is often considered the "father of botany" for his works on plants?

Quotation

Yes, I am positive that one of the great curatives of our evils, our maladies, social, moral, and intellectual, would be a return to the soil, a rehabilitation of the work of the fields.

Charles Wagner

100 Wordladder

Change one letter at a time (but not the position of any letter) to make a new word – and move from the word at the top of the ladder to the word at the bottom using the exact number of rungs provided.

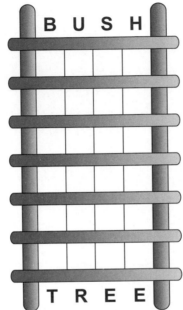

B U S H

T R E E

101 True or False

Can you decide whether the statement below is true or false?

Gardener and television presenter Rachel de Thame trained in classical ballet at The Royal Ballet School.

True or **False**

102 General Knowledge

See how many of the questions below you can correctly answer.

1 Dark in colour and growing up to four centimetres in length, the pest *Arion hortensis* is better known by what name?

2 'Miltonia', 'Encyclia', 'Vanda' and 'Maxillaria' are all genera of which flowering plant?

3 The lotus flower (*Nelumbo nucifera*) is the national flower of Vietnam and which other country?

4 What colour are the petals of the Star-of-Bethlehem flower (*Ornithogalum umbellatum*) that blooms in late spring/early summer?

5 'Mophead', 'lacecap', 'snowball', 'oakleaf' and 'paniculata' are all types of which shrub?

6 Name the tool similar to a pick but with one arm of the head curved like an adze and the other ending in a chisel edge or a point, used for breaking up hard ground, grubbing up trees, etc.

7 Which branch of science is concerned with the processes of the atmosphere, especially as a means of forecasting the weather?

8 What common name is given to the frothy mass on plants produced by the insect known as a froghopper?

9 A flowering plant of the *Asparagaceae* family, *Polygonatum multiflorum* is more commonly known as what?

Quotation

Trees and plants always look like the people they live with, somehow.

Zora Neale Hurston

94

Petal Puzzle

How many words of three or more letters can you make from those on the petals, without using plurals, abbreviations or proper nouns? The central letter must appear once in every word and no letter may be used more than once unless it is on a different petal. There is at least one nine-letter word to be found.

See how many of the questions below you can correctly answer.

1 Standing upright on the branches, what colour are the cones of the Korean fir (*Abies koreana*) before maturity?

2 'Hispi', 'Savoy' and 'January King' are all varieties of which vegetable?

3 In heraldry, the fleur-de-lis is a charge consisting of a stylised representation of which flower?

4 The first flexible hose was thought to have been made over 2,000 years ago from the intestines of which animal?

5 What nickname is given to the US State of Ohio, where trees of the horse-chestnut (genus *Aesculus*) are abundant?

6 Hybrid strains of which flowering perennial are associated with the name George Russell?

7 Which World War II campaign encouraged people to grow vegetables in gardens and parks, and on wasteland, to counter the shortage of food?

8 What name is given to the plant more commonly known as the Peruvian lily?

9 What term describes the condition where seedlings germinate and begin to grow well until whole trays rapidly collapse and die, due to the attack of soil-borne fungi in an excess of moisture?

Quotation

The home gardener is part scientist, part artist, part philosopher, part ploughman. He modifies the climate around his home.

John Whiting

105 Garden Borders

Fit the letters G, A, R, D, E and N into the grid in such a way that each horizontal row, each vertical column and each of the heavily bordered sections of six squares contains a different letter. Some letters are already in place.

			N		E
			D		
R		G			A
	D		R	A	

106 Garden Creatures Tracker

Starting at the top left corner and ending at the bottom right, track a path from letter to letter, in any direction except diagonally, in order to find the hidden garden creatures. All of the letters must be used once only.

G	R	E	E	I	D	E	A	P	D	M	Y	S	I	L	A	C
Y	L	F	N	P	M	R	E	H	I	A	L	N	A	B	L	K
L	A	D	W	S	O	U	S	T	T	Y	F	R	D	R	I	B
I	B	Y	E	S	P	I	R	H	I	B	B	A	I	R	P	S
R	D	C	R	T	A	R	L	W	I	G	G	N	U	R	S	L
W	T	U	H	M	G	N	I	R	A	S	T	A	Q	E	A	U
O	R	M	S	O	L	E	E	A	W	F	L	Y	S	L	W	G

Spot the Same

Which two butterflies are identical in every detail?

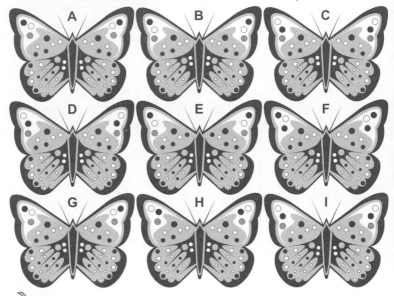

Spelling Bee

Which is the only one of the following to be correctly spelled?

a   ANTIRRHINUM

b   ANTERHINUM

c   ANTIRHINUM

d   ANTERRHINUM

Find the correct answer to each question from the four alternatives.

1 During the last ice age, which ended around 11,000 years ago, roughly by how much cooler was Earth's average temperature?
   a. 5 degrees Celsius   **b.** 8 degrees Celsius
   c. 10 degrees Celsius   **d.** 12 degrees Celsius

2 What is a 'blue moon'?
   a. It's blue in colour   **b.** Appears twice in same month
   c. It's blue around the rim **d.** It never happens

3 In which US state is Denali (also known as Mount McKinley, its former official name) North America's highest mountain?
   a. Washington   **b.** California
   c. Montana   **d.** Alaska

4 Excluding the Greenland Sea, how many of the world's seas have colours in their names?
   a. Seven   **b.** Six
   c. Four   **d.** Three

5 In which mountain range are the following volcanoes: Cotopaxi, Santa Ana, and Ojos del Salado?
   a. Urals   **b.** Altai Mountains
   c. Rocky Mountains **d.** Andes

6 The Sea of Marmara lies between the Black Sea and which other?
   a. Aegean   **b.** Adriatic
   c. White Sea **d.** Red Sea

7 Vatnajökull in Iceland, Jostedal in Norway and Aletsch in Switzerland are all types of which geographical feature?
   a. Lake   **b.** Glacier
   c. River   **d.** Plateau

See how many of the questions below you can correctly answer.

1   What are morels, shiitake and ceps?

2   Which fruit has varieties such as 'Merton Glory' and 'Napoleon Bigarreau'?

3   Which greenish-bronze grape (native to the basin of the river of North Carolina after which it is named) is used to make a sweet wine?

4   Which vegetable's botanical name is *Brassica napobrassica*?

5   Which widely-grown cereal grass is also known as Indian corn?

6   What sort of fruit is a spanspek?

7   Which red fruit comes from the plant *Rubus idaeus*?

8   Derived from Greek, which word defines an abnormal and persistent fear of flowers?

9   Often cooked in tomato sauce and sold in tins, what sort of beans are used to make baked beans?

10   By what name is the vegetable *Solanum tuberosum* more commonly known?

Quotation

It is only the farmer who faithfully plants seeds in the spring, who reaps a harvest in the autumn.

B C Forbes

Garden Maze

How successful will you be in trying to find a route to the centre of this garden maze?

112 Salad Sudoku

Every row, every column and each of the nine smaller boxes of nine squares should be filled with a different number from 1 to 9 inclusive. Some numbers are already in place. When the grid is completely filled, decode the numbers in the shaded squares, then rearrange the letters to spell out the name of a salad vegetable or fruit.

		8	7					
	6			2			1	
	4	9			1	6		
	2	3	6		7		4	
	7						2	
	9		2		4	3	7	
		2	5			4	9	
	5			1			8	
					2	7		

Code

1	2	3	4	5	6	7	8	9
A	C	D	H	I	O	R	S	Y

Answer: _____

102

See how many of the questions below you can correctly answer.

1 Destructive to plant roots, of which beetle is a wireworm the larva?

2 In which season of the year should wild varieties of bare-root roses be planted: late autumn or late winter – or midsummer?

3 Which species of rose is commonly planted to form a fast-growing, dense and bushy hedge?

4 Initiated by the British Tourist Board, which year saw the first Britain in Bloom campaign?

5 With yellow flesh and a distinctive flavour, which red-skinned main-crop potato was originally bred in the Netherlands in 1962?

6 Which large ornamental shrub (*B. davidii*) bears panicles of fragrant lilac-coloured flowers that attract butterflies?

7 Which pungent spice is the dried flower bud of a tropical myrtle, *Syzygium aromaticum*?

8 Victor Lemoine was a celebrated and prolific flower breeder who created many of today's lilac varieties. What was his nationality?

9 What term describes the warming-up of the Earth's surface due to the trapping of solar radiation which would otherwise be reflected back into space?

Quotation

I appreciate the misunderstanding I have had with Nature over my perennial border. I think it is a flower garden; she thinks it is a meadow lacking grass, and tries to correct the error.

Sara Stein

General Knowledge

See how many of the questions below you can correctly answer.

1 "Moses supposes his toeses are roses, but Moses supposes erroneously" was sung by Gene Kelly and Donald O'Connor in which film of 1952?

2 Butterflies and moths belong to which order of insects?

3 Yielding very hard wood, the quebracho tree is native to which continent?

4 By what common name do we know the tree *Pyrus communis*?

5 Which plants have an organ called a holdfast?

6 What does the adjective 'dasyphyllous' mean?

7 Which non-ministerial government department was set up in 1919 to expand Britain's forests and woodland after depletion during the First World War?

8 The dried root of which plant is used to treat rheumatism and skin complaints, as well as to flavour a carbonated drink?

9 In 2012, under the care of NASA astronaut Donald Pettit, what was the first flower to bloom aboard the International Space Station?

Quotation

I loved to get all dusty and ride horses and plant potatoes and cotton.

Dorothy Malone

Shape-up

Every row and column in this grid originally contained one bird, one flower, one leaf, one mushroom and two blank squares, although not necessarily in that order. Every symbol with a black arrow refers to the first of the four symbols encountered in the direction of the arrow. Every symbol with a white arrow refers to the second of the four symbols encountered in the direction of the arrow. Can you complete the original grid?

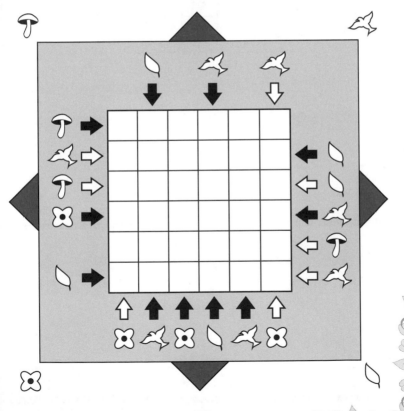

What's It Worth?

Each symbol stands for a different number. In order to reach the correct total at the end of each row and column, what is the value of the bird, flower, leaf and mushroom?

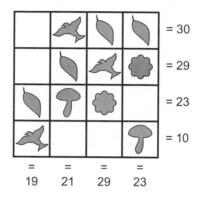

Shape Spotter

Which is the only shape to appear twice in exactly the same shading (black, white or green) in the box below? You'll need a keen eye for this one, as some shapes overlap others!

118 **Plants in Music**

See how many of the questions below you can correctly answer.

1   *I Heard it Through the Grapevine* is a song best known in a 1968 version by which singer?

2   A well-known version of *Tiptoe Through the Tulips* was recorded in 1968 by which falsetto-voiced singer?

3   *The Green Leaves of Summer* is a song that first appeared in a 1960 John Wayne film about an 1836 major event in US history. What was the film's title?

4   In 1966, *The Green Green Grass of Home* was a worldwide hit for which Welsh singer?

5   Which English folk song was parodied in a humorous version by Anthony Newley?

6   Which plants '… *Last in the Dooryard Bloom'd*': a poem by Walt Whitman that was set to music by German composer Paul Hindemith?

7   Which 'fruity' song was the only No 1 UK hit (in 1968) for the band The Move?

8   Specialising in bass guitar, double-bass and tuba, which musician formed Blue Mink in the 1960s, joined T. Rex in the 1970s, and (together with John Williams) formed Sky in the 1980s?

9   Which American hard rock band was formed by Axl Rose and others in 1985?

10 *A Rose by Any Name* is a song from the 2013 *Ghosts of Download* album by which American band?

119 General Knowledge

See how many of the questions below you can correctly answer.

1 Which one of these plants does not belong to the *Tanacetum* genus: tansy, feverfew, calendula, golden-buttons?

2 In botany, the word 'aculeate' describes a plant that is armed with what?

3 Which part of a flower's stamen produces pollen?

4 What word describes the organic component of soil, formed by the decomposition of leaves and other plant material by soil microorganisms?

5 'Campestra' and 'Napoli' are varieties of which vegetable?

6 What sort of creature is a hairstreak?

7 What name is given to the disorder when large, black/brown, leathery sunken pits appear on the bases of fruits such as tomatoes and peppers?

8 The first begonia was discovered in which South American country in 1690 by Charles Plumier, a Franciscan monk?

9 What type of plant is the eglantine, or sweet briar?

10 What colour are mistletoe berries?

Quotation

A garden is a complex of aesthetic and plastic intentions; and the plant is, to a landscape artist, not only a plant – rare, unusual, ordinary or doomed to disappearance – but it is also a colour, a shape, a volume or an arabesque in itself.

Roberto Burle Marx

120 Trailing Vine

The object of this puzzle is to trace a single path from the top left square to the bottom right square of the grid, moving through all of the cells in either a horizontal, vertical or diagonal direction. Every cell must be entered once only and your path should take you through the letters in the sequence V-I-N-E-V-I-N-E, etc. Can you find the logical way through?

V	I	V	I	V	I	N	E
I	N	E	N	E	N	I	V
N	V	E	N	I	V	V	N
E	N	E	I	E	E	I	E
V	I	V	V	I	N	V	N
I	V	E	V	E	N	E	I
N	I	N	N	I	I	V	N
E	V	E	V	I	N	E	E

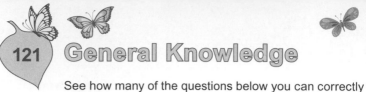

See how many of the questions below you can correctly answer.

1 Calvados is a brandy made in Normandy, France, with what type of fruit?

2 What colour are the berries of the juniper tree (*Juniperus communis*)?

3 What term is used to describe the method of growing plants in a controlled environment, in water containing nutrients?

4 With a distinctive flavour of celery and angelica, what plant is also known as 'Japanese parsley'?

5 The basic feature of what type of garden involves placing plants within regular geometric and symmetrical patterns picked out by evergreen herbs, planted in continuous ribbons?

6 Yielding an aromatic oil, and having lilac-blue flowers and ovate leaves, to which family of plants does the pennyroyal belong?

7 Which is the only native British pine (*Pinus sylvestris*)?

8 'Glen Moy', 'Glen Ample' and 'Glen Fyne' are all varieties of which fruit?

9 What culinary delicacy is a strong-smelling underground fungus that resembles an irregular, rough-skinned potato, and grows chiefly in broad-leaved woodland?

Quotation

When weeding, the best way to make sure you are removing a weed and not a valuable plant is to pull on it. If it comes out of the ground easily, it is a valuable plant.

Unknown author

122 Riddle-Me-Ree

Find one letter per line, following the clues given in the verse below. For example, 'My first is in houses, but never in homes' gives the letter U as the first letter. When you have finished, the letters will spell another word.

My first is in GORSE, as well as in BROOM,

My second's in FLOWER, and also in BLOOM,

My third's not in WASPS, though it is seen in BEES,

My fourth is in BIRCH, but never in TREES,

My fifth's not in SHORT, but it is found in LONG,

My whole is a bird with an all-year-round song.

1st	2nd	3rd	4th	5th	

123 True or False

Can you decide whether the statement below is true or false?

An epiphyte is a plant (especially one that is not parasitic) which grows on another plant.

True or False

111

Telephone Code

Use the telephone dial in order to spell out a quotation attributed to Francis Cabot Lowell.

6 6 3   5 4 3 3 8 4 5 3   4 8   6 3 9 3 7   3 6 6 9 3 4   8 6

1 2 2 6 5 6 5 4 8 4   6 6 3 ' 8   4 6 7 8 4 2 9 5 8 9 7 1 5

3 6 1 5 8 .   4 3   1   3 1 7 2 3 6   4 8   1   8 4 8 3   3 6 7

8 4 3   4 5 1 3 4 6 1 8 4 6 6 ,   4 6 9   2 1 6   9 3   1 3

9 3 7 0   3 1 7   3 7 6 5   8 4 3   1 3 3 4 6 6 4 6 3 ?

Find the correct answer to each question from the four alternatives.

1 What kind of creature is a red-eared slider?
a. Snake
b. Mouse
c. Terrapin
d. Butterfly

2 Which insects live in a formicary?
a. Wasps
b. Cockroaches
c. Termites
d. Ants

3 Fiddler, hermit and spider are three kinds of which decapod crustacean?
a. Crab
b. Shrimp
c. Lobster
d. Crayfish

4 Seismology is the scientific study of which natural phenomena?
a. Weather
b. Erosion
c. Ice sheets
d. Earthquakes

5 What is the term for the study of non-human animal behaviour?
a. Ethology
b. Virology
c. Axiology
d. Ichthyology

6 The cheetah is the fastest land animal on Earth. It can attain short-duration speeds of up to how many miles per hour?
a. 80
b. 75
c. 85
d. 60

7 Produced by the burning of fossil fuels, the increase of which gas in Earth's atmosphere is causing global warming?
a. Oxygen
b. Carbon dioxide
c. Nitrogen
d. Carbon monoxide

8 The roadrunner is a member of which family of birds?
a. Crow
b. Vulture
c. Cuckoo
d. Pigeon

See how many of the questions below you can correctly answer.

1 Which 1951 novel by John Wyndham, about alien plant life-forms, was made into a film released in 1963?

2 *The Pleasure Garden* was one of the earliest films to be directed by which English-born American?

3 Emma Orczy wrote which novel, set during the French Revolution, that was made into three films of the same title, the last one in 1982 starring Anthony Andrews, Jane Seymour and Ian McKellen?

4 Which 1989 film, based on Robert Harling's play of the same name concerns a group of women in a mid-west USA town? Sally Field and Dolly Parton were among the cast.

5 What is the title of John Christopher's 1956 novel regarding a vegetation-killing virus? It was made into a film in 1970 under a different title.

6 In which film does Morgan Freeman play the part of Jessica Tandy's character's chauffeur?

7 Which film with 'roses' in the title starred Michael Douglas, Kathleen Turner and Danny DeVito?

8 Who starred as Henry 'Dutch' Holland in the Ealing Studios' comedy *The Lavender Hill Mob?*

9 In the 1960 film *Please Don't Eat the Daisies*, which American singer makes this plea in the film's title song?

10 Based on John Steinbeck's novel of the same name, which film relates the story of the Joad family's flight from the 1930s Great Depression to a better life in California?

Spidoku

Each of the eight segments of the spider's web should be filled with a different number from 1 to 8, in such a way that every ring also contains a different number from 1 to 8. The segments run from the outside of the spider's web to the centre, and the rings run all the way around.
Some numbers are already in place. Can you fill in the rest?

Latin List

Pair up each of the numbered boxes on the left with the lettered boxes on the right to match the common names of plants with their botanical (or 'Latin') names.

1	Holly		a	*Viola*
2	Water lily		b	*Tagetes patula*
3	Love-in-a-mist		c	*Ilex*
4	Pansy		d	*Kniphofia*
5	Red-hot poker		e	*Nymphaea*
6	Bellflower		f	*Saxifraga x urbium*
7	French marigold		g	*Nigella damascena*
8	London pride		h	*Campanula*

Number	Letter
1	
2	
3	
4	

Number	Letter
5	
6	
7	
8	

See how many of the questions below you can correctly answer.

1 What name is given to the translucent, usually yellow, fossilised resin originating from extinct coniferous trees and used for ornaments and jewellery?

2. What term describes the removal of the growing tip of each stem between your thumb and forefinger in order to encourage bushier growth?

3 Which hard, durable timber used in shipbuilding and furniture-making comes from a large deciduous tree native to India and south-east Asia?

4 Which organ (modified from a stem, leaf, leaflet or stipule, for example) is used by climbing plants to cling to an object?

5 East Lambrook Manor in Somerset was the home of which famous gardener?

6 'Bryony Wade', 'Darren Pugh' and 'Kay Woolman' are all varieties of which flower?

7 Cultivated for its fragrant purple or blue flowers which are used in perfume, the heliotrope is a member of which family?

8 The trembling poplar (or aspen) belongs to which family of trees or shrubs?

9 Which tree that grows next to streams was once the major source of wood for making clogs in Britain?

Quotation

To dwell is to garden.

Martin Heidegger

Find the correct answer to each question from the four alternatives.

1 Of which US state is the mayflower the official flower?
- **a.** Alaska
- **b.** Nebraska
- **c.** Washington
- **d.** Massachusetts

2 Of which US state is the sego lily the official flower?
- **a.** Utah
- **b.** Connecticut
- **c.** New Jersey
- **d.** Arizona

3 Of which US state is the hawthorn the official flower?
- **a.** Virginia
- **b.** Wisconsin
- **c.** Idaho
- **d.** Missouri

4 Of which two US states is apple blossom the official flower?
- **a.** Maryland and Vermont
- **b.** Iowa and Kansas
- **c.** Arkansas and Michigan
- **d.** Montana and Oregon

5 Of which US state is the peony the official flower?
- **a.** Wyoming
- **b.** Illinois
- **c.** Delaware
- **d.** Indiana

6 Of which US state is the iris the official flower?
- **a.** Arkansas
- **b.** Tennessee
- **c.** New York
- **d.** Texas

7 Of which US state is the camellia the official flower?
- **a.** Alabama
- **b.** Florida
- **c.** California
- **d.** Hawaii

8 Of which US state is the sagebrush the official flower?
- **a.** Georgia
- **b.** Colorado
- **c.** Nevada
- **d.** West Virginia

Round the Block

You won't need a starting block to get you under way, because it isn't a race! Just arrange the six-letter solutions to the clues into the six blocks around each clue number. Write the answers in a clockwise or anticlockwise direction and you'll find that the last answer fits into the first; the main problem will be to decide in which square to put the first letter of each word…

When read in a clockwise direction (not necessarily starting at either of the topmost squares), the letters in the pale green squares spell out the name of a bird you might see in the garden.

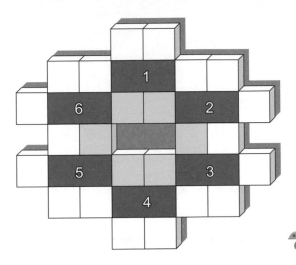

1. Relating to high mountains
2. Hot and fragrant spice
3. Reference point to shoot at
4. Walk lightly and stealthily
5. Be a sign of, indicate
6. Roller on a typewriter

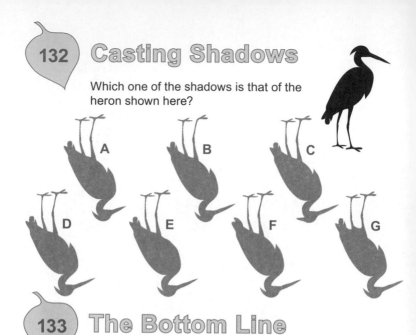

132 Casting Shadows

Which one of the shadows is that of the heron shown here?

133 The Bottom Line

The bottom line of this grid is waiting to be filled. Every square in the solution contains only one symbol from rows 1 to 5 above, although two or more squares in the solution may contain the same symbol. At the end of every numbered row is a score, which shows:

1 the number of symbols placed in the correct finishing position on the bottom line, as indicated by a tick; and

2 the number of symbols which appear on the bottom line, but in a different position, as indicated by a cross.

Can you fill each square with the correct symbol?

Score

1				✓ ✗
2				✓ ✗
3				✗ ✗
4				✗ ✗
5				✗
				✓✓✓✓

134 Multiple Choice

Find the correct answer to each question from the four alternatives.

1 Digitalis is a powerful cardiac stimulant prepared from the dried leaves of which plant?
   a. Potato   **b.** False nettle
   c. Foxglove   **d.** Hemlock

2 From what parts of the tree *Glycyrrhiza glabra* is juice extracted to make liquorice-flavoured confectionery?
   a. Roots   **b.** Leaves
   c. Seed pods (fruits)   **d.** Bark

3 Which of the following describes trees and shrubs that shed their leaves each year at the end of the period of growth?
   a. Boreal   **b.** Herbaceous
   c. Deciduous   **d.** Caducous

4 What name is given to the pollen-producing part of a flower, consisting of the anther and filament?
   a. Spadix   **b.** Style
   c. Stigma   **d.** Stamen

5 'Glaskin's Perpetual', 'Timperley Early', 'Valentine', and 'Victoria' are all varieties of which plant?
   a. Potato   **b.** Rhubarb
   c. Spinach   **d.** Asparagus

6 Occurring in many fruits and vegetables, which acid is largely responsible for the sour taste found in apples?
   a. Malic acid   **b.** Citric acid
   c. Formic acid   **d.** Oxalic acid

7 Which greyish powdery mould that causes a number of plant diseases is deliberately cultivated (as noble rot) on the grapes used for certain wines?
   a. Pythium   **b.** Ergot
   c. Sclerotinia   **d.** Botrytis

See how many of the questions below you can correctly answer.

1 A shoot originating from a bud on a root or a rhizome (sometimes at some distance from the stem of the plant) is known as what?

2 Which small tree or shrub bears distinctive four-lobed rosy-pink fruits and has the scientific name *Euonymus europaeus*?

3 What colour are the seeds contained in the pods of the false acacia tree (*Robinia pseudoacacia*)?

4 Which was England's first 'garden city'? (From 1903 First Garden City Ltd owned the entire estate.)

5 Owing to a high proportion of its land being used for food production, which US state was nicknamed 'The Garden State' in 1876, a name that was officially recognised in 1954?

6 Which perennial evergreen shrub (*Ruta graveolens*) has bitter strong-scented lobed leaves that are used in herbal medicine?

7 What was newspaper magnate Charles Foster Kane's dying word in Orson Welles' 1941 film *Citizen Kane*?

8 A Black Forest gateau is typically a chocolate cake layered with cream and which fruits?

9 Related to tobacco, which plant (of the family *Solanaceae*) has tubular flowers that are particularly fragrant at night?

Quotation

Land, then, is not merely soil; it is a fountain of energy flowing through a circuit of soils, plants, and animals.

Aldo Leopold

In Code

Each letter in the names of these plants is represented by a number which remains the same for that letter wherever it occurs on the page. Work out the code to reveal the common names of the plants. Some numbers are already decoded.

1	2	3	4	1	5	6	7
		W					

8	5	6	9	2	7	10	11	6

2	7	4	9	6	6	1	9	7	13	14
								U		

1	11	15	9	8	1	6	16	17	13	14
	L									

8	5	13	6	18	11	4	4	11

14	5	7	19	11	16
			K		

20	13	21	21	15	11

20	11	6	9	3	9	7	19	15	11
P									

2	22	13	9	15	11	18	9	2

137 Daffodil Dilemma

Ivor Dibber has been given a plan by his wife, who would like some daffodil bulbs to be planted in a square patch of grass. Mrs Dibber has made a grid map, showing the long-suffering Ivor exactly where the bulbs are to be planted, and she has decided to test Ivor's brain (and patience) by making a puzzle of it…

Those squares containing numbers are empty, but where a number appears in a square, it indicates how many daffodil bulbs are to be planted in the squares (up to a maximum of eight) surrounding the numbered one, touching it at any corner or side. There is only one bulb in any individual square.

Ivor needs your help. Place a circle into every square that should contain a daffodil bulb.

0			3		2	2			1
1		3		2				3	
2		3			2		3		2
4				3		4		4	
		4				4		4	2
			3		4				2
	4						2	4	
0				4					
	2		3	3		3			1
		1			1		0		0

See how many of the questions below you can correctly answer.

1   One of Shakespeare's most famous love scenes takes place when Romeo steals into a garden to talk to Juliet on her balcony. To which family does the garden belong?

2   "There sleeps Titania sometime of the night, lull'd in these flowers with dances and delight". From which play do these lines come?

3   Queen Gertrude scatters flowers over the grave of Ophelia in which of Shakespeare's tragedies?

4   In which play does Perdita declare that she prefers "hot lavender, mints, savory, marjoram" to "pied flowers"?

5   "When daisies pied, and violets blue, and lady-smocks all silver-white" comes from *Love's Labour's Lost.* What kinds of plant are lady-smocks (known today as lady's smocks)?

6   Who gives a warning to Prince Hal when he says "For though the camomile, the more it is trodden on the faster it grows, yet youth, the more it is wasted the sooner it wears."?

7   Can you complete this line from Shakespeare's Sonnet 99: "More flowers I noted, yet I none could see, but sweet or colour it had stol'n from …"

8   In which play does Cordelia say "They saw him just now as mad and deranged as the stormy sea, singing loudly, wearing a crown of nettles, thorns, hemlock and all the other weeds that grow in our cornfields."?

9   From which tragedy do the following lines come: "What's in a name? That which we call a rose, by any other name would smell as sweet."?

Each leaf contains either a true statement or a false statement, and your task is to begin at the one marked 'START', following a continuous line, travelling from leaf to touching leaf, until you reach the one marked 'END'. Every true statement is used in the path from 'START' to 'END', so there are no shortcuts, no paths may cross, nor can any leaf be used twice in order to reach your destination!

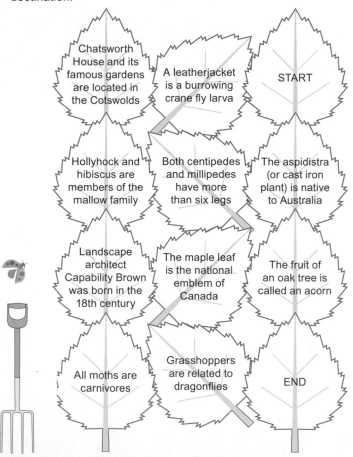

Chatsworth House and its famous gardens are located in the Cotswolds

A leatherjacket is a burrowing crane fly larva

START

Hollyhock and hibiscus are members of the mallow family

Both centipedes and millipedes have more than six legs

The aspidistra (or cast iron plant) is native to Australia

Landscape architect Capability Brown was born in the 18th century

The maple leaf is the national emblem of Canada

The fruit of an oak tree is called an acorn

All moths are carnivores

Grasshoppers are related to dragonflies

END

140 Nuts and Seeds

See how many of the questions below you can correctly answer.

1 An edible nut encased in a prickly shell is the product of which tree of the genus *Castanea*?

2 From which bean-like seed is chocolate obtained?

3 Oil extracted from the seeds of which plant is used in cooking, as salad oil, and in making margarine? This oil is also called benne or gingili oil.

4 What is the aromatic kernel of the tree *Myristica fragrans* more commonly called?

5 What is the name given to the aromatic seeds, of a flavour similar to liquorice, obtained from the umbelliferous plant *Pimpinella anisum?*

6 What nut is obtained from the *Areca catechu* palm?

7 Which commonly-grown fruit has its seeds (achenes) on the outside?

8 Which edible nut of the American hickory tree is similar to a walnut?

9 Which nut comes from the South American tree *Bertholletia excelsa?*

Quotation

The greatest gift of the garden is the restoration of the five senses.

Hannah Rion

141 Parks and Gardens

See how many of the questions below you can correctly answer.

1 Which national park borders the North Sea coast in the Whitby region?

2 Created by the landscape architects Brun, Penna and Schnitzler, and opened in 1994, the Jardin Atlantique is in which French city?

3 Historically, the most influential ancient gardens in the western world were Ptolemy's gardens. Where were they situated?

4 The Octagon Lake, The Oxford Bridge and The Lamport Gardens are all to be found in the grounds of which stately home?

5 Which castle in Kent is home to 'The Cloud Garden', built in winter 2009 by the team from Keder Greenhouse?

6 Which national park in the American state of Wyoming is famous for the 'Old Faithful' geyser?

7 *The Fabric of Nature* by Julia Hilton and *Monument to the Third Millenium* by Adrian Moakes are sculptures that are part of the Irwell Sculpture Trail in which park in Salford, Greater Manchester?

8 Some of which artist's most famous paintings were of the garden of his house in Giverny, famous for its rectangular Clos Normand?

9 With an exhibition of steppe plants, the Botanical Garden of Tver State University is the northernmost botanical garden in which country?

Quotation

God Almighty first planted a garden. And indeed, it is the purest of human pleasures.

Francis Bacon

Match the silhouettes of these leaves to the names of the trees on which they grow, as given in the list below.

1

2

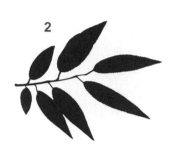

3

4

5

6

ASPEN   **ELM**

ASH   **OAK**

BIRCH   **WILLOW**

Honeycomb

Place the letters of each word, one per cell, so that every word flows in a clockwise direction around a number.

Where the hexagons of one word overlap with those of another, the letter in each cell is common to both.

When finished, rearrange the letters in the pale green hexagons to form the name of a root vegetable.

BAFFLE

BEHIND

COSINE

EVINCE

GYRATE

LARYNX

MENIAL

OCTAVE

ROLLED

STASIS

VECTOR

Answer: _____

See how many of the questions below you can correctly answer.

1 In 1969, Percy Thrower became the principal presenter of which regular TV gardening programme?

2 Starting in 1951, Percy carried out the design work for an English-style public garden in which European (then former) capital city?

3 During the 1970s and 1980s, Percy had a regular gardening slot on which children's TV programme?

4 Which title/medal was awarded to Percy by the Queen in 1984?

5 The Percy Thrower Garden Centre is located in which Shropshire town?

6 What is the Royal Horticultural Society's highest honour, with which Percy was awarded in 1977?

7 What name was given to the house and garden that Percy built on a one-and-a-half-acre site in 1963?

8 In 1975, Percy started a weekly gardening column for which daily newspaper?

9 Percy appeared in a sketch on which comedy duo's TV show in October 1971?

10 What was the breed of black dog with which Percy was often seen?

145 Flowers

See how many of the questions below you can correctly answer.

1   According to an old wives' tale, if you hold an open buttercup under someone's chin and their skin reflects the yellow of the flower, what does that indicate?

2   Bearing flowers in a range of colours on tall spikes, which flower of the genus *Alcea* is often seen in cottage gardens and includes varieties such as 'The Watchman' and 'Chater's Double'?

3   Valued for their patterned leaves, and flowers with upswept petals, to which family of plants does the cyclamen belong?

4   The Order of the Chrysanthemum is the highest order of chivalry in which country?

5   Bearing scented flowers, to which species of plants does the jonquil belong?

6   What is another name for the amaryllis, a bulbous plant with showy trumpet-shaped flowers?

7   What common name is given to *Aster novi-belgii*, that blooms around a saint's day, on 29 September?

8   What name is given to the cultivation of ornamental flowering plants for aesthetic purposes?

9   Christian missionaries adopted the unique structure of the flower of which plant as symbols of Christ's suffering and crucifixion?

10 Typically having spurred flowers marked with purple, yellow and white, and also known as 'heartsease' and 'love in idleness', *Viola tricolor* is the progenitor of which popular plant?

11 From which country was the tulip introduced to Europe in the 16th century?

Wordladder

Change one letter at a time (but not the position of any letter) to make a new word – and move from the word at the top of the ladder to the word at the bottom using the exact number of rungs provided.

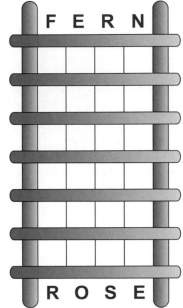

F E R N

R O S E

True or False

Can you decide whether the statement below is true or false?

Often seen growing in lawns, the common daisy (*Bellis perennis*) is a member of the *Ranunculaceae* family of plants.

True or False

See how many of the questions below you can correctly answer.

1 What name is given to the glass or plastic cover (originally bell-shaped) under which plants are forced or protected from frost?

2 Which children's television series featured puppets who spoke Oddle Poddle (their version of English) and lived either side of Little Weed?

3 What name is given to the pointed tool used for making holes for seeds or plants?

4 'Ashdown Forest', 'Hidcote', 'Loddon Blue' and 'Munstead' are all varieties of which flowering shrub?

5 What is the common name of *Ficus elastica*, a popular houseplant?

6 In 1984, the Eastern white pine became the official tree of which Canadian province?

7 John Tradescant (after whom the plant *Tradescantia* was named) succeeded his father as head gardener to which British king?

8 Which is the only species in the *Bromeliad* family grown commercially for its fruit?

9 What name is given to the sweet, sticky substance excreted by aphids?

Quotation

Some men like to make a little garden out of life and walk down a path.

Jean Anouilh

Petal Puzzle

How many words of three or more letters can you make from those on the petals, without using plurals, abbreviations or proper nouns? The central letter must appear once in every word and no letter may be used more than once unless it is on a different petal. There is at least one nine-letter word to be found.

See how many of the questions below you can correctly answer.

1 Which plant of the *Equisetum* genus is related to the ferns and has hollow jointed grooved stems and leaves reduced to nodal sheaths?

2 What is the more common name for the strelitzia?

3 What name is given to the fruits of the tree (*Malus sylvestris*) which are used to make a jelly served as an accompaniment to roast pork?

4 Which of the Channel Islands is associated with Royal potatoes?

5 Which tree (*Tilia europaea*) is also known as the linden?

6 Varieties of which flower include 'City of Bradford', 'Delft Blue', 'City of Haarlem' and 'Carnegie'?

7 The chief source of natural fluid in plants, what name is given to the substance that exudes when a plant is cut and coagulates on exposure to the air?

8 'Love apple' is an archaic name for which fruit?

9 What word describes trees that shed their leaves in autumn?

10 What colour is the crown (or cap) of a green woodpecker?

Quotation

Gardening requires lots of water – most of it in the form of perspiration.

Lou Erickson

Garden Borders

Fit the letters G, A, R, D, E and N into the grid in such a way that each horizontal row, each vertical column and each of the heavily bordered sections of six squares contains a different letter. Some letters are already in place.

	D	E			
			A		
A					
	G			N	
		R	E		
N	R				

Fruits and Nuts Tracker

Starting at the top left corner and ending at the bottom right, track a path from letter to letter, in any direction except diagonally, in order to find the hidden fruits and nuts. All of the letters must be used once only.

B	A	N	G	R	E	G	E	E	R	R	E	W	T	M	E	L
L	C	E	P	Y	E	A	Q	B	P	Y	M	A	U	C	N	O
A	C	K	B	R	N	G	U	A	S	L	I	L	N	H	E	R
D	N	O	E	R	C	N	I	R	N	C	I	R	P	A	Y	R
P	E	M	L	A	E	E	R	R	I	O	V	E	S	T	R	A
C	A	M	O	O	O	B	P	Y	K	T	I	P	R	E	B	W
H	L	E	N	G	S	E	U	M	P	O	L	E	A	R	R	Y

137

Spot the Same

Which two watering cans are identical in every detail?

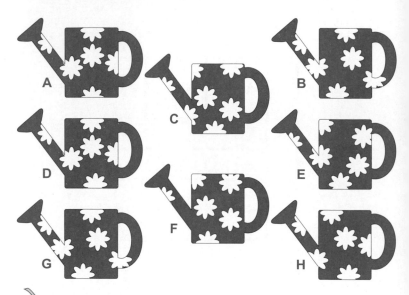

154

Spelling Bee

Which is the only one of the following to be correctly spelled?

a   POLYANTHERS

b   POLLYANTHERS

c   POLLYANTHUS

d   POLYANTHUS

138

Find the correct answer to each question from the four alternatives.

1 The desman is a member of which family of animals?
  a. Rat   **b.** Mole
  c. Mouse   **d.** Shrew

2 Nicknamed 'Methuselah', one of the world's oldest known living trees stands in California. How old is it estimated to be?
  a. 5,000 years   **b.** 4,000 years
  c. 3,500 years   **d.** 4,500 years

3 What is the common name for a beaver's home?
  a. Bank   **b.** Dam
  c. Lodge   **d.** Burrow

4 Which abundant sea crustacean is the staple food of the blue whale?
  a. Shrimp   **b.** Langoustine
  c. Prawn   **d.** Krill

5 Which word means the opposite of hibernation: ie the state of inactivity during the summer months?
  a. Fasciation   **b.** Supination
  c. Depuration   **d.** Aestivation

6 What kind of flower is *Rafflesia arnoldii*, the world's largest flower bloom?
  a. Sunflower   **b.** Rhododendron
  c. Lily   **d.** Dahlia

7 What term describes animals and plants that have both male and female organs and characteristics?
  a. Aphrodite   **b.** Hermaphrodite
  c. Hermaphobe   **d.** Endosperm

156 Gardens in Literature

See how many of the questions below you can correctly answer.

1 Daphne du Maurier's novel *Rebecca* deals with the struggles of a young woman haunted by the spectre of her husband's beautiful first wife. In the book's opening, she has a disturbing dream in which the gardens of which estate are completely overgrown?

2 In the final book of Philip Pullman's *His Dark Materials* trilogy, the protagonists, Lyra and Will, promise to sit on a bench in which garden for an hour on Midsummer's Day every year?

3 In which 1958 novel does a lonely young boy called Tom, living in an urban apartment block, slip out one night to discover a magical garden that existed there many years ago?

4 In which children's novel by Frances Hodgson Burnett does an unhappy orphan named Mary Lennox rediscover a forgotten garden in her uncle's gloomy Yorkshire estate?

5 In which of Chaucer's *Canterbury Tales* does an elderly man named Januarie build a beautiful walled garden for his young wife, May?

6 Which work by Voltaire ends with the phrase "mais il faut cultiver notre jardin" (but we must cultivate our garden)?

7 In whose garden did Christopher Boone find a dead dog in Mark Haddon's *The Curious Incident of the Dog in the Night-time*?

8 Which villa (or castle) and its gardens feature in the novel *The Enchanted April* by Elizabeth Von Arnim?

Quotation

Gardening is how I relax. It's another form of creating and playing with colours.

Oscar de la Renta

Garden Maze

How successful will you be in trying to find a route to the centre of this garden maze?

158 Salad Sudoku

Every row, every column and each of the nine smaller boxes of nine squares should be filled with a different number from 1 to 9 inclusive. Some numbers are already in place. When the grid is completely filled, decode the numbers in the shaded squares, then rearrange the letters to spell out the name of a salad vegetable or fruit.

3			4	9			8	
	6			7			2	3
8	9		3					
5	3				6			
			8				7	1
					3		1	8
7	1			2			3	
	5			8	1			7

Code

1	2	3	4	5	6	7	8	9
A	C	E	B	O	P	R	S	T

Answer: _____

142

See how many of the questions below you can correctly answer.

1 By what name is the vegetable 'courgette' known in the USA?

2 Often served with fish, which sauce chiefly consists of mayonnaise, chopped gherkins, capers and herbs?

3 What name is given to the elongated part of a carpel, or group of fused carpels, between the ovary and the stigma?

4 What name is given to the single-seeded and winged fruit of the ash tree?

5 Beechnuts (the small triangular brown fruit of the beech, pairs of which are enclosed in a prickly case) and acorns (the fruit of the oak) are traditionally used to fatten which farm animals?

6 Which word describes the branches and foliage of a tree, as well as the protective upper layer of a forest?

7 Which deciduous flowering shrub with clusters of colourful, sometimes fragrant flowers, gets its name from the Greek word for 'dry', because the shrub flourishes in that type of soil?

8 Which aquatic plant plays a central role in Indian religions such as Hinduism, Buddhism, Sikhism, and Jainism?

9 What name is given to the fine spores that contain male gametes that are borne by an anther in a flowering plant?

Quotation

I say, if your knees aren't green by the end of the day, you ought to seriously re-examine your life.

Bill Watterson

General Knowledge

See how many of the questions below you can correctly answer.

1   Which anti-malarial drug is obtained from the yellow cinchona plant?

2   Which tropical tree has a sweet, reddish-black acidic pulp used to make drinks and medicines?

3   Which tree of the genus *Corylus* is also called a cob or filbert?

4   Between which three fruits is the Ugli a cross?

5   First found in the Netherlands, which destructive disease of elms is caused by infestation with the fungus *Ceratocystis ulmi* and spread by bark beetles?

6   'Marjorie's Seedling' and 'Early Laxton' are varieties of which fruit?

7   What is the fruit of the *Pyrus* tree?

8   The Gimlet is a cocktail made of gin and the juice of which fruit?

9   Which ornamental shrubby climbing plant, widely cultivated in the tropics, has insignificant flowers surrounded by large, brightly coloured papery bracts which persist on the plant for a long time, and was named after a French explorer?

Quotation

He plants trees to benefit another generation.

Caecilius Statius

161 Shape-up

Every row and column in this grid originally contained one bird, one flower, one leaf, one mushroom and two blank squares, although not necessarily in that order. Every symbol with a black arrow refers to the first of the four symbols encountered in the direction of the arrow. Every symbol with a white arrow refers to the second of the four symbols encountered in the direction of the arrow. Can you complete the original grid?

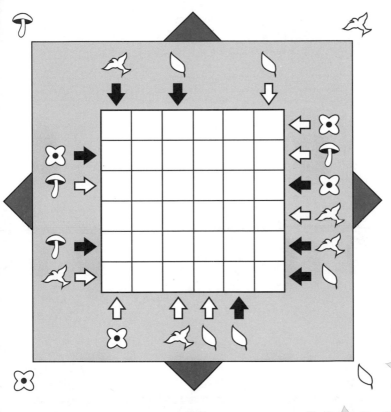

162 What's It Worth?

Each symbol stands for a different number. In order to reach the correct total at the end of each row and column, what is the value of the bird, flower, leaf and mushroom?

bird	flower	flower		= 39
mushroom	bird	leaf	flower	= 42
	mushroom	flower		= 27
mushroom	leaf		mushroom	= 30
= 33	= 42	= 36	= 27	

163 Shape Spotter

Which is the only shape to appear twice in exactly the same shading (black, white or green) in the box below? You'll need a keen eye for this one, as some shapes overlap others!

146

See how many of the questions below you can correctly answer.

1 In the Flanders and Swann song *Misalliance*, the love affair between which two plants is doomed because they grow spirally in opposite directions?

2 Who composed the symphonic poem *Tapiola*, a depiction in sound of his native Finland's vast forests?

3 Which band was known for its one-hit wonder *Green Tambourine*, the title track to their debut album?

4 *Cracklin' Rose* (or *Cracklin' Rosie*) was a smash hit for which singer-songwriter in 1970?

5 With which song did The Hollies reach No 3 on its original release in 1969, then reach No 1 on its re-release almost 20 years later?

6 *Pines of Rome, Fountains of Rome* and *Roman Festivals* were written by which Italian composer (1879–1936)?

7 *Tie a Yellow Ribbon Round the Ole Oak Tree* was a 1973 No 1 hit for which band (featuring Tony Orlando)?

8 *We'll Gather Lilacs in the Spring,* recorded by many singers including Julie Andrews and Frank Sinatra, was written by which Welsh composer of musicals?

9 Who was the female lead singer of the Black Rose Band? The band's only album (released in 1980) is entitled *Black Rose*.

10 Written by Fats Waller, which song with 'honeysuckle' in the title has been recorded by dozens of singers including Marlene Dietrich, Eva Cassidy and Louis Armstrong?

See how many of the questions below you can correctly answer.

1 Related to the citruses, which orange-like fruit of the genus *Fortunella* has an edible sweet rind and acid pulp?

2 What colour are the petals of the roses 'Leonardo da Vinci', 'Baroness Rothschild, 'Mark Twain' and 'Gertrude Jekyll'?

3 By what name is *Impatiens walleriana* more commonly known?

4 'Ebony', 'Ben Lomond' and 'Baldwin' are varieties of which fruit?

5 Which country was the birthplace (possibly as early as 100 BC) of the wheelbarrow?

6 What type of vegetables are mangetout and marrowfat?

7 *Libertia grandiflora*, also known as the 'satin flower', is native to which country of the southern hemisphere?

8 What is the name of Monty Don's garden in Herefordshire, situated some eight miles from the Welsh border?

9 Which BBC2 series followed a year in Carol Klein's garden at Glebe Cottage in north Devon?

10 The tree *Macadamia integrifolia* (which produces macadamia nuts) is native to which country?

Quotation

When a finished work of 20th century sculpture is placed in an 18th century garden, it is absorbed by the ideal representation of the past, thus reinforcing political and social values that are no longer with us.

Robert Smithson

166 Trailing Vine

The object of this puzzle is to trace a single path from the top left square to the bottom right square of the grid, moving through all of the cells in either a horizontal, vertical or diagonal direction. Every cell must be entered once only and your path should take you through the letters in the sequence V-I-N-E-V-I-N-E, etc. Can you find the logical way through?

V	N	E	E	V	I	E	V
I	N	V	N	I	V	N	I
V	E	I	V	E	N	E	N
N	I	N	E	I	N	V	I
I	E	I	V	I	E	I	N
N	V	E	E	N	V	V	E
E	N	V	N	E	E	I	V
V	I	I	V	I	N	N	E

General Knowledge

See how many of the questions below you can correctly answer.

1 The leaves of which tree are the preferred diet of the silkworm?

2 What word describes a non-native plant (such as Japanese knotweed) that spreads to a degree believed to cause damage to the environment, the economy or human health?

3 By what name is *Physalis alkekengi* better known, due to its having an inflated basal calyx that matures into a papery orange fruit covering?

4 A popular favourite for hanging baskets, petunias are native to which continent?

5 Celtuce is a cultivar of which vegetable?

6 *Raphanus sativus* is the scientific name for which salad vegetable?

7 Which English garden designer coined the term 'landscape gardening' in order to express his theory that the art requires: "the united powers of the landscape painter and the practical gardener"?

8 The flag of which country features a green cedar on a white background between two red stripes?

9 Sauerkraut is a dish made of the finely cut leaves of which vegetable?

Quotation

To forget how to dig the earth and to tend the soil is to forget ourselves.

Mahatma Gandhi

168 Riddle-Me-Ree

Find one letter per line, following the clues given in the verse below. For example, 'My first is in houses, but never in homes' gives the letter U as the first letter. When you have finished, the letters will spell another word.

My first is in BUTTERFLY, never in LARVA,

My second's in GRAPEFRUIT, KUMQUAT and GUAVA,

My third is in BEETLE, but not seen in BUG,

My fourth is in SNAIL, but isn't in SLUG,

My fifth is in PRICKLE, though it's not found in STING,

My whole is a plant that blooms in the spring.

1st	2nd	3rd	4th	5th

169 True or False

Can you decide whether the statement below is true or false?

A loganberry is a cross between a blackcurrant and a raspberry.

True or False

Use the telephone dial in order to spell out a quotation attributed to D Elton Trueblood.

1   516   418   5123   18   53188   1   88178

66   2482693746 3   843   5316463   63

49516   5433   9436   43   651688   84123

87338   96237   94424   43   46698   3955

9355   43   9455   63937   848.

Multiple Choice

Find the correct answer to each question from the four alternatives.

1 What name is given to the Japanese art of flower-arranging?
- **a.** Origami
- **b.** Kirigami
- **c.** Ikebana
- **d.** Bonsai

2 Famed for its Walled Garden, in which county is Lydiard Park?
- **a.** Wiltshire
- **b.** Derbyshire
- **c.** Lancashire
- **d.** Dorset

3 Of which popular bedding plant are 'African', 'French' and 'Signet' all types?
- **a.** Dahlia
- **b.** Marigold
- **c.** Lily
- **d.** Lupin

4 'Gustus', 'Montgomery', 'Crispus', 'Titus' and 'Clodius' are all varieties of which vegetable?
- **a.** Broccoli
- **b.** Carrot
- **c.** Cauliflower
- **d.** Brussels sprouts

5 Which of the following is not a variety of pea?
- **a.** Little Marvel
- **b.** Hurst Green Shaft
- **c.** Scarlet Emperor
- **d.** Kelvedon Wonder

6 How many petals has a flower of the night-scented stock?
- **a.** Three
- **b.** Four
- **c.** Five
- **d.** Six

7 Thought to be at least 3,000 years old, what kind of tree stands in the churchyard of the village of Fortingall in Perthshire?
- **a.** Ash
- **b.** Oak
- **c.** Sequoia
- **d.** Yew

8 Derris is a powder derived from the roots of the woody climbing plants of the genus *Derris*. As what is it used?
- **a.** Insecticide
- **b.** Rodenticide
- **c.** Herbicide
- **d.** Fungicide

See how many of the questions below you can correctly answer.

1 The botanic gardens of which city features several glasshouses, the most notable of which is the Kibble Palace?

2 Which of these trees can grow the tallest: the silver fir (*Abies alba*) or the noble fir (*Abies procera*)?

3 What colour are the blooms of *Lobelia cardinalis*?

4 The Dutch Bridge, Heron Wood Reserve (including the Crypto-gramic Sanctuary), Dynamo Pond, and Sargent's Garden are all features of which botanic garden?

5 Which invasive plant (*Heracleum mantegazzianum*) has sap containing chemicals that can cause photodermatitis, where the skin becomes very sensitive to sunlight and may suffer blistering, pigmentation and long-lasting scars?

6 The home of the Plant Heritage National Collection of Autumn Flowering Asters, what is the name of the garden situated at Colwell, in the Malvern Hills, Worcestershire?

7 To which genus of plants do the dogwoods belong?

8 Housing the largest collection of pressed, dried plant specimens in Australia, the Australian National Botanic Gardens are in which city?

9 The National Council for the Conservation of Plants and Gardens (NCCPG) adopted which new name in 2009?

10 Cultivars of which plant include the Grandiflorum types with varieties such as 'Summer Nights' and 'Blue Butterfly', and the (taller) Elatum types with varieties such as 'Blue Dawn' and 'Atholl'?

Spidoku

Each of the eight segments of the spider's web should be filled with a different number from 1 to 8, in such a way that every ring also contains a different number from 1 to 8.
The segments run from the outside of the spider's web to the centre, and the rings run all the way around.
Some numbers are already in place. Can you fill in the rest?

Latin List

Pair up each of the numbered boxes on the left with the lettered boxes on the right to match the common names of plants with their botanical (or 'Latin') names.

1	Busy Lizzie		a	*Petroselinum crispum*

2	Speedwell		b	*Alcea*

3	Periwinkle		c	*Myosotis*

4	Cedar of Lebanon		d	*Ulex europaeus*

5	Gorse		e	*Impatiens*

6	Hollyhock		f	*Vinca*

7	Forget-me-not		g	*Cedrus libani*

8	Parsley		h	*Veronica*

Number	Letter
1	
2	
3	
4	

Number	Letter
5	
6	
7	
8	

See how many of the questions below you can correctly answer.

1 Born in England in 1895, Edna Margaret Walling was one of which country's most influential landscape designers?

2 What is the name of the UK's largest, most high-tech green-house complex?

3 'Peace', 'Fragrant Cloud' and 'Queen Elizabeth' are all varieties created by which flamboyant rose breeder?

4 The fernlike leaves of which herb are used to flavour dishes such as gravlax?

5 What colour are the ripe fruits of the lingonberry, most commonly used in Scandinavian countries to make lingonberry jam?

6 Who wrote a best-selling series of gardening manuals that include *The Vegetable & Herb Expert* and *Be Your Own Vegetable Doctor*?

7 *Ribes sanguineum*, the flowering currant, was introduced into cultivation by 19th century Scottish botanist David Douglas and is native to which continent?

8 What name is given to the agave fibre used for making ropes and matting? Its name comes from the port in Yucatán, Mexico from where it was first exported.

9 'Cambridge Favourite', 'Mara de Bois', 'Aromel' and 'Honeoye' are all varieties of which fruit?

Quotation

Use plants to bring life.

Douglas Wilson

Find the correct answer to each question from the four alternatives.

1 What is fly agaric?

   a. An insecticide   **b.** A fungus

   c. A lubricant   **d.** A lizard

2 What is the common name of the plant *Allium cepa*?

   a. Green pepper   **b.** Red pepper

   c. Onion   **d.** Leek

3 Jacamars, found in the forests of South and Central America are what kinds of creatures?

   a. Birds   **b.** Cats

   c. Wild dogs   **d.** Frogs

4 Named after the place where it was first bred, Beveren in Belgium, what kind of creature is a Blue Beveren?

   a. Dog   **b.** Cat

   c. Hamster   **d.** Rabbit

5 Introduced around the world as an ornamental tree, the weeping willow (*Salix babylonica*) is native to which country?

   a. China   **b.** Iran

   c. Iraq   **d.** India

6 Found only in the rainforests of New Guinea, of which creature is the Goliath birdwing one of the largest?

   a. Fruit bat   **b.** Flying fox

   c. Vampire bat   **d.** Butterfly

7 The adjective 'vulpine' relates to which animals?

   a. Wolves   **b.** Foxes

   c. Badgers   **d.** Otters

Round the Block

You won't need a starting block to get you under way, because it isn't a race! Just arrange the six-letter solutions to the clues into the six blocks around each clue number. Write the answers in a clockwise or anticlockwise direction and you'll find that the last answer fits into the first; the main problem will be to decide in which square to put the first letter of each word…

When read in a clockwise direction (not necessarily starting at either of the topmost squares), the letters in the pale green squares spell out the name of a bird you might see in the garden.

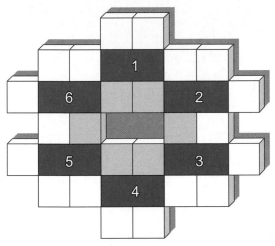

1 Someone performing servile work

2 Warm blooded vertebrate creature

3 Hind portion of a side of bacon

4 Former name of the Chinese city of Beijing

5 Venomous snakes

6 Capital of Austria

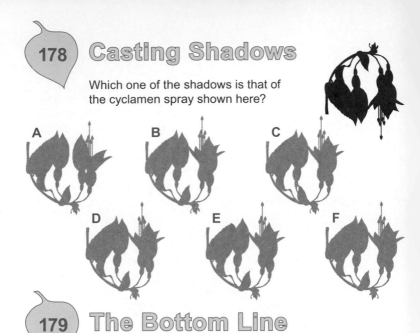

178 Casting Shadows

Which one of the shadows is that of the cyclamen spray shown here?

A B C

D E F

179 The Bottom Line

The bottom line of this grid is waiting to be filled. Every square in the solution contains only one symbol from rows 1 to 5 above, although two or more squares in the solution may contain the same symbol. At the end of every numbered row is a score, which shows:

1 the number of symbols placed in the correct finishing position on the bottom line, as indicated by a tick; and

2 the number of symbols which appear on the bottom line, but in a different position, as indicated by a cross.

Can you fill each square with the correct symbol?

				Score
1				X X
2				X X
3				X X
4				X
5				✓
				✓✓✓✓

160

See how many of the questions below you can correctly answer.

1 "Why are there trees I never walk under but large and melodious thoughts descend upon me?" is a line from *Song of the Open Road*, penned by whom?

2 "Beloved, gaze in thine own heart, The holy tree is growing there; From joy the holy branches start, And all the trembling flowers they bear." These are the first four lines of which poem by William Butler Yeats?

3 "Through primrose tufts, in that green bower, The periwinkle trailed its wreaths; And 'tis my faith that every flower, Enjoys the air it breathes." is the third verse from *Lines Written in Early Spring* by which poet?

4 "The violets in the mountains have broken the rocks" are words from *Camino Real* and appear on the tombstone of which poet and playwright?

5 Which flower is most often used in Emily Dickinson's poetry to depict feminine figures?

6 "Summer set lip to earth's bosom bare, And left the flushed print in a poppy there." These lines are from *The Poppy*, written by whom?

7 Who instructed us to "Pluck not the wayside flower, It is the traveller's dower" in his poem *Wayside Flowers*?

8 Which Scottish poet penned "O my Luve's like a red, red rose, That's newly sprung in June"?

9 "Perfumes are the feelings of flowers" is from *Die Harzreise* (*The Harz Journey*), a report about a trip to the Harz Mountains by which German poet and author?

See how many of the questions below you can correctly answer.

1 What causes green top, a condition where the tops of carrot roots become green?

2 Which North American vine of the genus *Parthenocissus* is grown mainly for its very decorative red autumnal foliage?

3 When a plant such as lettuce sends up a flower stalk and goes to seed, the condition is referred to as what?

4 What name is given to the condition affecting tomatoes whereby the area around the stalk remains hard and fails to ripen, due to too little potash or too much sunlight?

5 The aromatic fruits of which herb are used to flavour seed cake?

6 Which herb (*Salvia officinalis*) includes the varieties 'purple', 'Dalmatian' and 'broadleaf'?

7 Name the cartoon character who gains extra strength in times of need by consuming spinach.

8 The US state of Nebraska is informally nicknamed the Cornhusker State. Who or what is a cornhusker?

9 In cookery, what French name is given to a sachet of herbs used as flavouring and removed before the dish is served?

Quotation

Remember that children, marriages, and flower gardens reflect the kind of care they get.

H Jackson Brown, Jr

In Code

Each letter in the names of these plants is represented by a number which remains the same for that letter wherever it occurs on the page. Work out the code to reveal the common names of the plants. Some numbers are already decoded.

1	2	3	4	5

6	2	6	7
			Y

8	9	10	6	2	11	6	12	13	4	5
								W		

14	12	5	15	4

8	14	4	15	1	16	10	1

3	7	17	15	12	17	14	2	6	9
	P								

18	2	8	14	9	4	6	18	9	15

19	9	2	15	7
D				

8	4	6	9	16	19	2	16	4

20	9	8	9	5	9	16	19	9
J								

1	9	5	5	9	3	12	16

Ivor Dibber has been given a plan by his wife, who would like some daffodil bulbs to be planted in a square patch of grass. Mrs Dibber has made a grid map, showing the long-suffering Ivor exactly where the bulbs are to be planted, and she has decided to test Ivor's brain (and patience) by making a puzzle of it…

Those squares containing numbers are empty, but where a number appears in a square, it indicates how many daffodil bulbs are to be planted in the squares (up to a maximum of eight) surrounding the numbered one, touching it at any corner or side. There is only one bulb in any individual square.

Ivor needs your help. Place a circle into every square that should contain a daffodil bulb.

1	2					3		2	1
			1			4		2	
	3	3			5			2	
1		3				4			2
	3			5			3		1
2			2					4	3
	5	4		2	3				
	5					3	4	6	
		5		2	2				
	2	2		1			2	3	

Find the correct answer to each question from the four alternatives.

1 What is the common name for the plant *Dionaea muscipula* that feeds on insects?
- **a.** Lobster pot
- **b.** Pitcher plant
- **c.** Venus flytrap
- **d.** Funnel plant

2 Capucin, spider, howler and squirrel are all species of which animal?
- **a.** Baboon
- **b.** Monkey
- **c.** Gorilla
- **d.** Marmoset

3 Which marine creature lives in cast-off mollusc shells for protection?
- **a.** Hermit crab
- **b.** Whelk
- **c.** Spider crab
- **d.** Abalone

4 What class of cold-blooded invertebrates comprises frogs, toads, newts, salamanders and caecilians?
- **a.** Cetacea
- **b.** Reptilia
- **c.** Gastropoda
- **d.** Amphibia

5 What name is given to the dry, treeless grassland of Central Asia?
- **a.** Prairie
- **b.** Savanna
- **c.** Steppe
- **d.** Veldt

6 The genus *Muscardinus* relates to which mammal?
- **a.** Field mouse
- **b.** Common shrew
- **c.** Dormouse
- **d.** Hedgehog

7 Which is the largest big cat of the Americas?
- **a.** Jaguar
- **b.** Cougar
- **c.** Ocelot
- **d.** Caracal

Each leaf contains either a true statement or a false statement, and your task is to begin at the one marked 'START', following a continuous line, travelling from leaf to touching leaf, until you reach the one marked 'END'. Every true statement is used in the path from 'START' to 'END', so there are no shortcuts, no paths may cross, nor can any leaf be used twice in order to reach your destination!

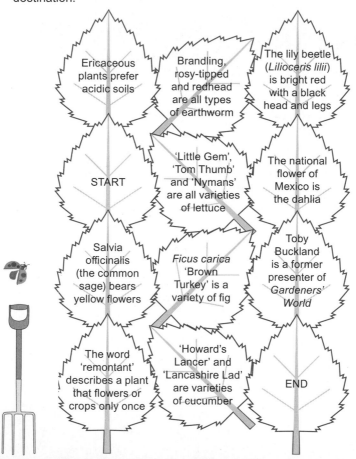

Ericaceous plants prefer acidic soils

Brandling, rosy-tipped and redhead are all types of earthworm

The lily beetle (*Lilioceris lilii*) is bright red with a black head and legs

'Little Gem', 'Tom Thumb' and 'Nymans' are all varieties of lettuce

START

The national flower of Mexico is the dahlia

Salvia officinalis (the common sage) bears yellow flowers

Ficus carica 'Brown Turkey' is a variety of fig

Toby Buckland is a former presenter of *Gardeners' World*

The word 'remontant' describes a plant that flowers or crops only once

'Howard's Lancer' and 'Lancashire Lad' are varieties of cucumber

END

166

See how many of the questions below you can correctly answer.

1 Approximately how many millions of trees did Britain lose to The Great Storm of 1987?

2 Which branch of biology deals with the distribution of animals and plants over the world?

3 Widely used in brewing, what are 'Goldings', 'Fuggle' and 'Admiral'?

4 Kirsch is an alcoholic spirit distilled from the fermented juice of which fruit?

5 In which northern European country is tropical fruit grown in greenhouses heated from natural hot springs?

6 Where is home to 'The National Fruit Collection', comprising more than 4,000 varieties of fruit?

7 What is the name for the condition in plants of excessive production of leaves at the expense of fruit or flower production?

8 Which gardener's habit of discussing the 'capabilities of improvement' of a property earned him the nickname by which he is best known?

9 Which nocturnal insectivorous migratory bird, *Caprimulgus europaeus*, has grey-brown cryptic plumage and a distinctive churring call?

Quotation

Just because you've only got houseplants doesn't mean you don't have the gardening spirit: I look upon myself as an indoor gardener.

Sara Moss-Wolfe

General Knowledge

187

See how many of the questions below you can correctly answer.

1 In the 15th century, which two rival branches of the royal House of Plantagenet fought the Wars of the Roses…?

2 …and of these, which adopted the red rose as its symbol?

3 Owing to its popular and widely-distributed crop, which US state is nicknamed 'The Potato State'?

4 Of what kind of tree is 'General Sherman' the world's largest living specimen?

5 What more common name is given to seasonal rhinitis, suffered by many people and resulting from an allergic reaction to pollen?

6 What name is given to the white, dusty coating on the leaves, stems and flowers of plants caused by a group of related fungi?

7 'Boltardy' and 'Burpees Golden' are varieties of which root vegetable?

8 The common toadflax (*Linaria vulgaris*) bears flowers of what colour?

9 The first-known garden gnomes were made of clay and produced in which European country in the 1800s, where they became known as Gartenzwerge (garden dwarfs)?

Quotation

I love decorating my home. I'm a gardener too, so that's usually something I have to play catch-up with.

Suzy Bogguss

Identity Parade

Match the silhouettes of these flowers to their names in the list below.

1

2

3

4

5

6

AQUILEGIA　　**MARIGOLD**
BLEEDING HEART　　**POPPY**
LILY　　**TULIP**

Place the letters of each word, one per cell, so that every word flows in a clockwise direction around a number.

Where the hexagons of one word overlap with those of another, the letter in each cell is common to both.

When finished, rearrange the letters in the pale green hexagons to form the name of a herb.

ADVISE
AUTUMN
DANGLE
EQUATE

GUNMEN
LIGNUM
NETTED

PAYOUT
SNEEZE
TUMULT
VOYAGE

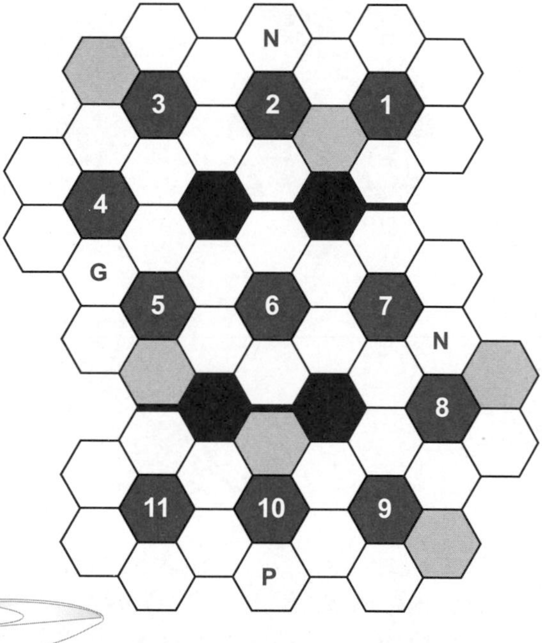

N
3 2 1
4
G
5 6 7
N
8
11 10 9
P

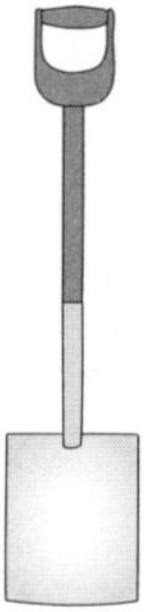

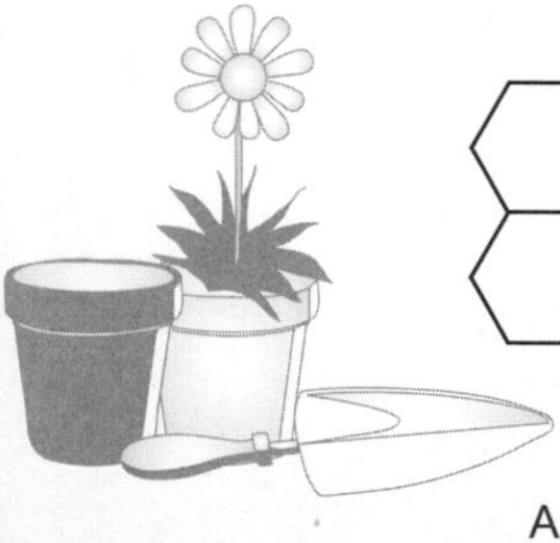

Answer: _____

Find the correct answer to each question from the four alternatives.

1 In which well-known West Yorkshire spa town was Alan Titchmarsh born in May 1949?

2 Alan's first appearances on TV were on which BBC One news and current affairs programme which ran from 1969 to 1983?

3 Co-presenters Tommy Walsh and Charlie Dimmock appeared with Alan in which garden makeover programme?

4 What common title is given to a range of practical gardening books written by Alan and published by BBC Books?

5 Published in 2001, what is the title of Alan's first fiction book?

6 On which radio station has Alan had a Saturday morning programme since 2012?

7 What shorter name was adopted in 2009 by The National Council for the Conservation of Plants and Gardens, of which Prince Charles is the patron and Alan Titchmarsh the president?

8 What is the name of the garden gnome for whom Alan provides a voice in the children's TV series '… the Garden Gnome'?

9 In a newspaper interview in December 2014, Alan suggested he had sympathetic views toward which political party?

10 When appearing on BBC TV's *Breakfast* in June 2015, Alan used a (legitimate) alternative term for 'double digging' that caused some embarrassment to the show's presenter. What was the term used?

191 General Knowledge

See how many of the questions below you can correctly answer.

1 Which twining vine of the genus *Ipomoea*, with funnel-shaped flowers, is named after a time of day?

2 Which root vegetable includes the varieties 'Wilhelmsburger', 'Marian', 'Angela' and 'Magres'?

3 Which Garden City in Hertfordshire was founded by Sir Ebenezer Howard in the 1920s?

4 In botany, what is a petiole?

5 In which year was The Royal Horticultural Society founded as the Horticultural Society of London (it gained its present name in a Royal Charter granted in 1861)?

6 The rose varieties 'Dawn Chorus', 'Remember Me' and 'Brilliant Sweet Dreams' all bear blooms of what colour?

7 The nuts from what type of tree are traditionally used to make pesto sauce?

8 Known to Americans as arugula, by what name is the salad plant *Eruca sativa* known in Britain?

9 Which vegetable is widely recognised as the national symbol of Wales?

Quotation

A garden was the primitive prison, till man with Promethean felicity and boldness, luckily sinned himself out of it.

Charles Lamb

192) Wordladder

Change one letter at a time (but not the position of any letter) to make a new word – and move from the word at the top of the ladder to the word at the bottom using the exact number of rungs provided.

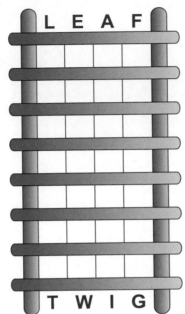

L E A F

T W I G

193) True or False

Can you decide whether the statement below is true or false?

The Jerusalem artichoke was introduced to Europe by Crusaders returning from campaigns in the Middle East.

True or **False**

General Knowledge

See how many of the questions below you can correctly answer.

1 Which gardener created Barnsdale Gardens for the BBC's *Gardeners' World...*?

2 ...and in which county is Barnsdale Gardens?

3 Supported by the Big Lottery Fund and led by Kew, which project inspires people to come together to transform local spaces by sowing, growing and enjoying native flowers?

4 Norton in Hales was crowned 'Champion of Champions' in the RHS Britain in Bloom competition 2015. In which county is Norton in Hales?

5 Which nuts are used to make marzipan?

6 Used for more than 150 years as an insecticide, pyrethrum is extracted from the flower-heads of which genus of plants?

7 The drink cassis is made from which fruit?

8 'Galia', 'Cantaloupe', 'Ogen' and 'Honeydew' are all varieties of which fruit?

9 What colour is the dye that can be produced from the leaves of the woad plant *Isatis tinctoria...*?

10 ...and what colour are the petals of the woad flower?

Quotation

The secret of improved plant breeding, apart from scientific knowledge, is love.

Luther Burbank

Petal Puzzle

How many words of three or more letters can you make from those on the petals, without using plurals, abbreviations or proper nouns? The central letter must appear once in every word and no letter may be used more than once unless it is on a different petal. There is at least one nine-letter word to be found.

See how many of the questions below you can correctly answer.

1 The garden pansy belongs to which genus of plants?

2 Which succulent plant yields a gel widely used in the cosmetics and alternative medicine industries, and has many claimed therapeutic properties?

3 'Mirabelle de Nancy', 'Early Laxton', 'Jubilee Dessert' and 'Victoria' are all varieties of which fruit?

4 A cyclamen flower normally has how many reflexed petals?

5 Lychees are fruits of an evergreen tree native to which country?

6 What is meant by the word 'viridiflora' when it appears in the names of plants?

7 The first Hampton Court Palace Flower Show was held in July of which year?

8 Which English garden designer, journalist and television personality is the son of the novelist Margaret Drabble?

9 Which former presenter of BBC's *Gardeners' World* launched an online plant nursery in 2011 that is based at Powderham Castle in Devon?

10 The auricula is an alpine primula with leaves said to resemble the ears of which animal?

Quotation

I never had any other desire so strong, and so like to covetousness, as that one which I have had always, that I might be master at last of a small house and large garden.

Abraham Cowley

197 Garden Borders

Fit the letters G, A, R, D, E and N into the grid in such a way that each horizontal row, each vertical column and each of the heavily bordered sections of six squares contains a different letter. Some letters are already in place.

		N			G
				E	R
			G		
D				A	
	R				
			E		

198 Herbs and Spices Tracker

Starting at the top left corner and ending at the bottom right, track a path from letter to letter, in any direction except diagonally, in order to find the hidden herbs and spices. All of the letters must be used once only.

C	H	O	M	E	D	O	R	E	H	E	L	N	D	E	M	I
R	E	C	F	L	I	B	A	G	Y	R	T	E	I	G	A	N
V	I	L	R	I	L	L	O	S	S	R	H	E	V	E	S	T
A	S	Y	E	M	O	M	P	P	A	O	Y	M	E	G	N	A
F	T	A	R	L	C	A	L	E	R	S	R	E	L	O	S	E
F	N	A	R	E	N	N	O	G	S	Y	P	P	I	R	A	M
R	O	G	O	N	F	E	V	A	L	E	E	P	C	A	R	Y

199 Spot the Same

Which two hanging baskets are identical in every detail?

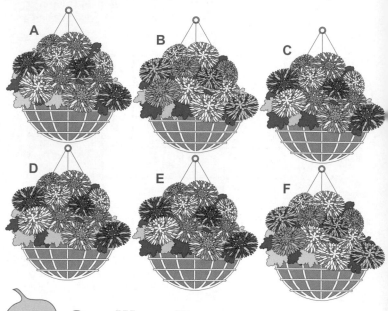

200 Spelling Bee

Which is the only one of the following to be correctly spelled?

a WIEGELA

b WEIGELLA

c WEIGELA

d WIEGELLA

178

201 Genera Knowledge

Find the correct answer to each question from the four alternatives.

1 Which one of these plants does not belong to the *Brassica* genus?
   a. Turnip   **b.** Cauliflower
   c. Carrot   **d.** Swede

2 Which one of these plants does not belong to the *Artemisia* genus?
   a. Sagebrush   **b.** Wormwood
   c. Tarragon   **d.** Rosemary

3 Which one of these plants does not belong to the *Prunus* genus?
   a. Peach   **b.** Almond
   c. Quince   **d.** Plum

4 Which one of these plants does not belong to the *Rubus* genus?
   a. Blackberry   **b.** Strawberry
   c. Raspberry   **d.** Dewberry

5 Which one of these plants does not belong to the *Narcissus* genus?
   a. Jonquil   **b.** Primrose
   c. Daffodil   **d.** Paperwhite

6 Which one of these plants does not belong to the *Ranunculus* genus?
   a. Campion   **b.** Crowfoot
   c. Buttercup   **d.** Celandine

7 Which one of these plants does not belong to the *Dianthus* genus?
   a. Carnation   **b.** Sweet William
   c. Pink   **d.** Candytuft

8 Which one of these plants does not belong to the *Solanum* genus?
   a. Potato   **b.** Chicory
   c. Aubergine   **d.** Woody nightshade

See how many of the questions below you can correctly answer.

1 Which fast-growing species of cypress is renowned for being the cause of disputes with neighbours whose own property becomes overshadowed?

2 What is the national flower of Russia?

3 Gregor Mendel was an Augustinian monk and botanist whose experiments in breeding which plants led to his eventual recognition as founder of the science of genetics?

4 By what more common name is the tree *Euonymus europaeus* better known, its wood being used to make items used in the wool industry?

5 Which plant of the genus *Nepeta* has downy leaves, purple-spotted white flowers, and a pungent smell attractive to felines?

6 What word describes the placing of seeds in moist sand, peat, etc, in layers, to preserve them or to promote germination?

7 What is the most common colour of the flowers of the grape hyacinth (*Muscari*)?

8 Which plant of the dandelion family is cultivated for its leaves which are used as a salad vegetable, and has roots that are baked, ground and used as a coffee substitute?

9 'Captivator', 'Invicta' and 'Whinham's Industry' are varieties of which fruit?

Quotation

A garden must combine the poetic and be mysterious with a feeling of serenity and joy.

Luis Barragan

203 Garden Maze

How successful will you be in trying to find a route to the centre of this garden maze?

204 Salad Sudoku

Every row, every column and each of the nine smaller boxes of nine squares should be filled with a different number from 1 to 9 inclusive. Some numbers are already in place. When the grid is completely filled, decode the numbers in the shaded squares, then rearrange the letters to spell out the name of a salad vegetable or fruit.

		1			4			6
8	7		6			2		
6					5			
9	5							
	1	3	5		6	7	2	
							3	5
			4					7
		9			7		6	1
1			8			5		

Code

1	2	3	4	5	6	7	8	9
B	C	E	M	O	R	S	T	U

Answer: _____

See how many of the questions below you can correctly answer.

1 Which part of the madder plant (*Rubia*) contains an organic compound called alizarin, that gives its red colour to a textile dye known as rose madder?

2 What aid to seed dispersal is employed by *Galium aparine*, a plant nicknamed variously as goosegrass, cleavers, etc?

3 *Melissa officinalis*, known as lemon balm, is a member of which family of plants?

4 What word describes a plant or grouping of plants selected for desirable characteristics that can be maintained by propagation?

5 Whose published works of 1736 include *Fundamenta Botanica* and *Bibliotheca Botanica*?

6 With stems bearing single yellow flowers, and often seen growing wild on banks on the sides of lanes, what is the more common name for *Primula vulgaris*?

7 What herb, sometimes called cilantro, has leaves used as seasoning or garnish, and aromatic fruit used for flavouring?

8 What name is commonly given to the fungus *Phallus impudicus*, in which the gleba emits a powerful stench?

9 The wood of which tree is traditionally used to make black piano keys?

Quotation

It pleases me to take amateur photographs of my garden, and it pleases my garden to make my photographs look professional.

Robert Brault

See how many of the questions below you can correctly answer.

1 In the children's books by Beatrix Potter, what was the name of the gardener intent upon keeping hungry rabbits out of his vegetable garden?

2 What are tines?

3 *Acacia pycnantha*, commonly called the golden wattle, is a tree native to (and is the national floral emblem of) which country?

4 'Chrysler Imperial', 'Double Delight', 'Fragrant Cloud' and 'Peace' are all varieties of what type of rose?

5 What colour are the flowers of Mount Etna broom (*Genista aetnensis*)?

6 What term describes the moving of plants from a protected, stable environment to changeable, harsher outdoor conditions?

7 Which cereal crop is most commonly affected by *Claviceps purpurea*, an ergot fungus?

8 When crushed, the leaves of the disc (or rayless) mayweed (*Matricaria discoidea*) smell of which fruit, giving rise to an alternative common name for the plant?

9 Which mainly tropical grasshopper migrates in vast swarms that cause extensive damage to vegetation?

Quotation

A well-tended garden is better than a neglected wood lot.

Dixie Lee Ray

207 Shape-up

Every row and column in this grid originally contained one bird, one flower, one leaf, one mushroom and two blank squares, although not necessarily in that order. Every symbol with a black arrow refers to the first of the four symbols encountered in the direction of the arrow. Every symbol with a white arrow refers to the second of the four symbols encountered in the direction of the arrow. Can you complete the original grid?

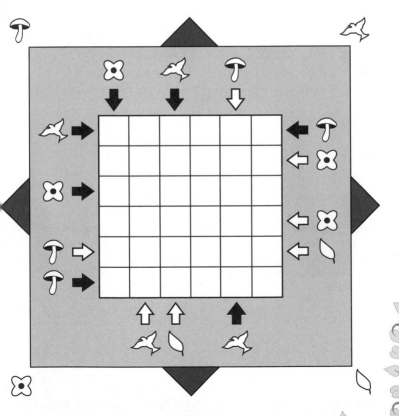

208) What's It Worth?

Each symbol stands for a different number. In order to reach the correct total at the end of each row and column, what is the value of the bird, flower, leaf and mushroom?

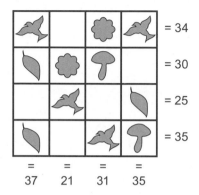

209) Shape Spotter

Which is the only shape to appear twice in exactly the same shading (black, white or green) in the box below? You'll need a keen eye for this one, as some shapes overlap others!

210 **Plants in Music**

See how many of the questions below you can correctly answer.

1 Together with Algerian musician Cheb Mami, which British artist recorded the song *Desert Rose*, a Top Twenty hit in 1999?

2 The children's nursery rhyme *Ring a Ring o' Roses* is widely believed to have been inspired by which event in history?

3 Can you complete these words to the chorus of the song *Lemon Tree*, written by Will Holt: "Lemon tree, very pretty and the lemon flower is sweet, But the fruit of the poor lemon …"?

4 Which song with 'ivy' in the title has been covered by The Rolling Stones, Manfred Mann, The Dave Clark Five and The Hollies?

5 *Hyacinth House* is a track from the album *L.A. Woman*: by which band?

6 (*I Never Promised You a*) *Rose Garden* is a song made famous by which female country music singer?

7 *Roses from the South* is a piece written by which famous composer of waltzes?

8 Which song with a wild flower in the title proved to be a big hit for The Foundations?

9 Paul Weller wrote *English Rose* a track that appears on *All Mod Cons*, an album by which band?

10 *Blumine* (the German approximation of 'floral') is a discarded movement from the earliest symphony of which Austrian composer, perhaps best known for his *Adagietto,* used in the film *Death in Venice*?

211 Birds

See how many of the questions below you can correctly answer.

1 Feeding almost exclusively on ants, what sort of a bird is a wryneck?

2 The genus *Corvus* relates to which family of birds?

3 Which wild duck is the ancestor of most domestic breeds of duck?

4 Which bird has 'honey' and 'rough-legged' varieties?

5 Which bird is the nearest relative of the cassowary?

6 'Blue', 'coal' and 'long-tailed' are types of which bird?

7 What colour is the plumage of a female blackbird?

8 To which family of birds does the roadrunner belong?

9 By what common name do we know the colourful bird *Erithacus rubecula*, a frequent visitor to gardens?

10 What collective noun is used to describe a group of crows?

11 What type of bird is a yaffle?

12 Which raucous black and white member of the crow family is attracted to bright objects?

Quotation

I am sure that if you plant the trees back again, it will do nothing but good.

Michael Fish

Trailing Vine

The object of this puzzle is to trace a single path from the top left square to the bottom right square of the grid, moving through all of the cells in either a horizontal, vertical or diagonal direction. Every cell must be entered once only and your path should take you through the letters in the sequence V-I-N-E-V-I-N-E, etc. Can you find the logical way through?

V	I	E	V	I	V	N	E
E	N	N	N	E	I	V	I
V	E	I	N	V	E	E	N
I	N	V	E	I	N	I	V
N	I	E	V	I	I	V	N
E	V	V	N	V	N	I	E
N	I	N	V	E	I	V	N
E	V	I	E	I	N	E	E

See how many of the questions below you can correctly answer.

1 'Old Knobbley' in Mistley, Essex, dates from the 13th century. What kind of tree is 'Old Knobbley'?

2 Deodar is the hard sweet-smelling wood from which type of tree in the Himalayas?

3 Evergreen yacca trees (*Podocarpus coriacea* and *Podocarpus purdieana*) are native to which region of the Caribbean Basin and North Atlantic Ocean?

4 Most commonly used as a Christmas tree, by what name is the tree *picea abies* better known?

5 The gourd of which tree can be used as a container for liquid or the bowl of a tobacco pipe?

6 What is another name for the mountain ash of the genus *Sorbus?*

7 What name is given to the downy, hanging flowering spikes of trees such as the willow and hazel?

8 What term describes a tree or shrub that is trained to grow flat against a wall, supported by a lattice?

9 Timber from trees is divided into which two main descriptive types?

10 Which tree has 'English', 'white' and 'slippery' varieties?

Quotation

The greatest fine art of the future will be the making of a comfortable living from a small piece of land.

Abraham Lincoln

214 Riddle-Me-Ree

Find one letter per line, following the clues given in the
verse below. For example, 'My first is in houses, but never
in homes' gives the letter U as the first letter. When you have finished,
the letters will spell another word.

My first's not LUPIN, but it is found in PHLOX,

My second's in HEDGEHOG, as well as in FOX,

My third is in POPLAR, though never in ASH,

My fourth's not in RAINDROP, but is seen in SPLASH,

My fifth's not in PEACH, but it is found in CHERRY,

My whole is a plant that bears a red berry.

1st	2nd	3rd	4th	5th

215 True or False

Can you decide whether the statement below is true or
false?

As a member of the genus *Solanum*, the aubergine is related to both
the tomato and the potato.

Telephone Code

Use the telephone dial in order to spell out a quotation attributed to Liberty Hyde Bailey.

4 3   1   6 3 7 8 6 6   2 1 6 6 6 8   5 6 9 3   1

6 5 1 6 8   1 3 8 3 7   4 3   4 1 8   6 7 9 6 3 2

4 8 ,   8 4 3 6   4 3   4 1 8   3 4 8 4 3 7   2 6 6 3

1   6 6 6 7   4 6 1   6 7   4 8   2 3 9 6 4 2   6 3

3 5 6 8 4 6 6 .

Myth, Legend and Folklore

See how many of the questions below you can correctly answer.

1 Daphne, a nymph who rejected the love of the Greek god Apollo, was turned into what tree or bush?

2 Who was the Roman goddess of flowering plants?

3 In classical mythology, nymphs known as dryads lived in what?

4 Which poisonous and narcotic Mediterranean plant of the nightshade family was formerly credited with magical and medicinal properties because of the supposedly human shape of its forked fleshy root?

5 Which plant is said to bring luck, should you find one with four lobes?

6 In Greek mythology, who was the god of the north wind?

7 Which flower was said to cover the Elysian Fields of Greek legend?

8 Which widely-distributed verbena was long believed to have great magical and medicinal powers?

9 Widely used as a Christmas decoration, which parasitic plant was venerated by the Druids, who cut it ceremonially from their sacred oak with a golden knife?

Quotation

Weather means more when you have a garden. There's nothing like listening to a shower and thinking how it is soaking in around your green beans.

Marcelene Cox

See how many of the questions below you can correctly answer.

1 Which modern-day plant hunter established the World Garden of Plants at Lullingstone Castle in Kent? In 2000, he was kidnapped by gunmen in South America and held captive for nine months.

2 Which Scottish botanist died in Hawaii in 1834 after falling into a bull pit? An American native conifer is named after him.

3 In which English county is Clapham, the home village of Reginald Farrer (1880–1920), an intrepid plant hunter who experimented in seeding by loading a shotgun with seeds and blasting them into cliff faces close to his home?

4 Which French botanist accompanied the German explorer Baron von Humboldt in expeditions during the early nineteenth century?

5 Botanist and naturalist Carl Linnaeus, the man who gave us the standard system of naming all living things (eg human = *homo sapiens*), was a native of which European country?

6 Captain James Cook's first global voyage, of 1768–71, carried with it which great botanist and plant hunter?

7 George Forrest is perhaps best known for his discoveries of many new species of which plants in the Chinese province of Yunnan during the early twentieth century?

8 Covering several other fields of study as well as botany, the Lewis and Clark expedition of 1804–06 crossed much of which country?

9 Scottish botanist Robert Fortune (1812–80) is famous as the man who took tea plants from China in 1848 and planting them in which other Asian country?

Spidoku

Each of the eight segments of the spider's web should be filled with a different number from 1 to 8, in such a way that every ring also contains a different number from 1 to 8. The segments run from the outside of the spider's web to the centre, and the rings run all the way around. Some numbers are already in place. Can you fill in the rest?

Pair up each of the numbered boxes on the left with the lettered boxes on the right to match the common names of plants with their botanical (or 'Latin') names.

| 1 | Golden rod |
| a | *Aquilegia* |

| 2 | Fig |
| b | *Foeniculum vulgare* |

| 3 | Crab apple |
| c | *Solidago* |

| 4 | Sea holly |
| d | *Delphinium consolida* |

| 5 | Columbine |
| e | *Malus sylvestris* |

| 6 | Larkspur |
| f | *Antirrhinum* |

| 7 | Snapdragon |
| g | *Ficus carica* |

| 8 | Fennel |
| h | *Eryngium maritimum* |

Number	Letter
1	
2	
3	
4	

Number	Letter
5	
6	
7	
8	

See how many of the questions below you can correctly answer.

1 Which deciduous and semi-deciduous trees comprise the genus *Ulmus*?

2 The larva of what type of insect is a chafer grub, which can be very destructive to plant roots?

3 'Jerusalem' being a corruption of its Italian name 'girasole', the Jerusalem artichoke (*Helianthus tuberosus*) is a species of which tall garden flower?

4 Which of the following birds has a red patch over the bill and on the throat: swift, swallow, house martin, sand martin?

5 If the name of a plant (*Aspohodelus aestivus*, for example) includes the word 'aestivus', it indicates that it flowers in which season of the year?

6 Also called the Scottish flame flower and flame nasturtium, *Tropaeolum speciosum* is native to which South American country?

7 Which was the first property that the National Trust acquired for its garden?

8 'Musselburgh', 'Toledo' and 'Atlanta' are varieties of which vegetable?

9 Which tree bears white flowers from which 'champagne' can be made, and later bears bluish-black berries used by many home winemakers?

Quotation

Gardening is not a rational act.

Margaret Atwood

Find the correct answer to each question from the four alternatives.

1 Which bear is the world's largest?
   a. Black bear   **b.** Brown bear
   c. Polar bear   **d.** Giant panda

2 The bark of the tree, *Salix alba* was used in the production of which common drug?
   a. Aspirin   **b.** Paracetamol
   c. Pethedine   **d.** Codeine

3 The 1976 Barcelona Convention was set up to resolve serious pollution problems in which sea?
   a. Aegean Sea   **b.** Mediterranean
   c. Black Sea   **d.** North Sea

4 Which bird feeds by holding its head upside down underwater and filtering out algae and marine molluscs through its beak?
   a. Crane   **b.** Avocet
   c. Heron   **d.** Flamingo

5 The Athenian philosopher Socrates was sentenced to death by drinking which poison?
   a. Strychnine   **b.** Hemlock
   c. Henbane   **d.** Cyanide

6 Which vulture gets its name from the old belief that it would take live lambs?
   a. Lammergeier   **b.** Condor
   c. Rüppell's vulture   **d.** Griffon

7 Becoming extinct in 1936, what kind of animal was the thylacine?
   a. Marsupial monkey   **b.** Marsupial mouse
   c. Marsupial dog   **d.** Marsupial bird

Round the Block

You won't need a starting block to get you under way, because it isn't a race! Just arrange the six-letter solutions to the clues into the six blocks around each clue number. Write the answers in a clockwise or anticlockwise direction and you'll find that the last answer fits into the first; the main problem will be to decide in which square to put the first letter of each word...

When read in a clockwise direction (not necessarily starting at either of the topmost squares), the letters in the pale green squares spell out the name of a bird you might see in the garden.

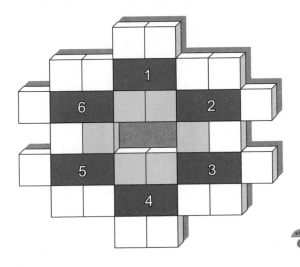

1 Fairly certain, almost sure to happen

2 Capital of the Philippines

3 Polish port city formerly called Danzig

4 Spirit distilled from malted grain

5 Old Testament book of prophecies

6 Woven shopping bag

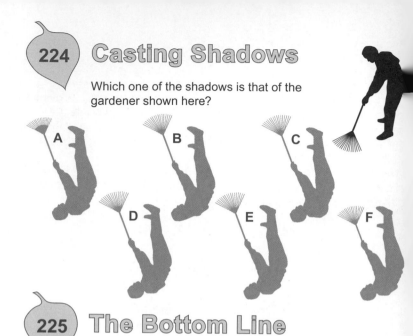

224 Casting Shadows

Which one of the shadows is that of the gardener shown here?

A   B   C

D   E   F

225 The Bottom Line

The bottom line of this grid is waiting to be filled. Every square in the solution contains only one symbol from rows 1 to 5 above, although two or more squares in the solution may contain the same symbol. At the end of every numbered row is a score, which shows:

1 the number of symbols placed in the correct finishing position on the bottom line, as indicated by a tick; and

2 the number of symbols which appear on the bottom line, but in a different position, as indicated by a cross.

Can you fill each square with the correct symbol?

				Score
1				X X
2				X X
3				X X
4				X X
5				X X
				✓✓✓✓

226 Multiple Choice

Find the correct answer to each question from the four alternatives.

1 Found on sand dunes, heaths and other dry areas, what colour are the petals of the common centaury (*Centaurium erythraea*)?
a. White
b. Yellow
c. Pink
d. Blue

2 Water, field and bank are the three species found in Britain of which creature?
a. Rat
b. Otter
c. Mink
d. Vole

3 Barnacle, Brent, Canada and greylag are all what type of birds?
a. Swans
b. Geese
c. Gulls
d. Ducks

4 What type of creature is a slow-worm?
a. Snake
b. Worm
c. Lizard
d. Beetle

5 By what name is the creature *Talpa europaea* better known?
a. Field mouse
b. Vole
c. Mole
d. Squirrel

6 Females of the peacock butterfly lay their egg clusters on the underside of the leaves of which plant?
a. Groundsel
b. Sorrel
c. Burdock
d. Nettle

7 The Atlas cedar (*Cedrus atlantica*) is native to which two countries?
a. Algeria and Morocco
b. USA and Canada
c. Spain and Portugal
d. Britain and Ireland

8 Which acid contributes to the sourness of green apples and is noticeably present in rhubarb?
a. Salicylic acid
b. Malic acid
c. Lactic acid
d. Citric acid

227 Parks and Gardens

See how many of the questions below you can correctly answer.

1 Wales has three national parks: two are the Pembrokeshire Coast and Snowdonia – which is the third?

2 By what name are The Royal Botanic Gardens in Richmond, London known?

3 Perhaps the most widely-known arboretum in the UK, which arboretum was established in 1829 by Robert Stayner Holford?

4 What is the name of the garden at the Duke of Cornwall Spinal Treatment Centre at Salisbury Hospital, created in 2012 as a memorial to the schoolboy (after whom it was named) killed by a polar bear while on an expedition in Norway?

5 Created by Catherine de Medici, which public garden is located between the Louvre Museum and the Place de la Concorde in the 1st arrondissement of Paris?

6 Which London park contains the Serpentine, Rotten Row and Speakers' Corner?

7 Famous for its rhododendrons, in which garden can you explore a Himalayan valley amid the mountains of north Wales?

8 Whernside, Ingleborough and Pen-y-Ghent are the Three Peaks of which UK national park?

9 Which attraction is sited in Jubilee Gardens on London's South Bank and opened in January 2000?

10 Where is Sir George Frampton's statue of Peter Pan?

Quotation

It was such a pleasure to sink one's hands into the warm earth, to feel at one's fingertips the possibilities of the new season.

Kate Morton

In Code

Each letter in the names of these plants is represented by a number which remains the same for that letter wherever it occurs on the page. Work out the code to reveal the common names of the plants. Some numbers are already decoded.

1	2	3	4	5	6	4	7	5	8

9	10	11	11	7	1	12	4	13	1	7	2
W											

11	10	8	13	1

14	2	11	8
B			

15	10	11	2	6	12	13	1	7	5	8

16	13	6	1	17	11	13	9	10	6
				F					

8	10	3	10	8	14	6	18	2	1	4	19	10	8	5	8
							Y								

2	3	15	2	6	2	12	5	3

3	16	13	6	20	13	1	10	6	2
				Z					

229 Daffodil Dilemma

Ivor Dibber has been given a plan by his wife, who would like some daffodil bulbs to be planted in a square patch of grass. Mrs Dibber has made a grid map, showing the long-suffering Ivor exactly where the bulbs are to be planted, and she has decided to test Ivor's brain (and patience) by making a puzzle of it…

Those squares containing numbers are empty, but where a number appears in a square, it indicates how many daffodil bulbs are to be planted in the squares (up to a maximum of eight) surrounding the numbered one, touching it at any corner or side. There is only one bulb in any individual square.

Ivor needs your help. Place a circle into every square that should contain a daffodil bulb.

2	2			2	2	1	2		1
		3			3			2	
				2		3	4		
1		4	3			4			
	3				2			6	
						3		3	
0			2			3	1		
	1	1			4				1
	2				3	3	4	3		1
1								2	

Find the correct answer to each question from the four alternatives.

1 Which birds have the highest metabolic rate of all animals (insects excepted)?
- **a.** Budgerigars
- **b.** Wrens
- **c.** Kingfishers
- **d.** Hummingbirds

2 How many species of domestic dog are there in the world today?
- **a.** One
- **b.** Five
- **c.** Fifty
- **d.** Five hundred

3 At ten feet and six inches, which South American vulture has the greatest wingspan of any bird (except certain waterbirds)?
- **a.** Lammergeier
- **b.** Golden eagle
- **c.** Andean condor
- **d.** King vulture

4 What is the better-known name of the maidenhair tree?
- **a.** Ginkgo biloba
- **b.** Japanese fir
- **c.** Monkey puzzle
- **d.** Persian palm

5 Which Australasian bird is the largest of the kingfisher family?
- **a.** Macaw
- **b.** Honeyeater
- **c.** Forest kingfisher
- **d.** Laughing kookaburra

6 Earl Grey tea is flavoured with the oil of which plant?
- **a.** Persimmon
- **b.** Bergamot
- **c.** Lemon
- **d.** Lime

7 In which mountain range are the Paine Mountains?
- **a.** Rocky Mountains
- **b.** European Alps
- **c.** New Zealand Alps
- **d.** Andes

8 At around 645 days, which mammal has the longest gestation period?
- **a.** Asian elephant
- **b.** Giraffe
- **c.** African elephant
- **d.** Hippopotamus

True or False Maze

Each leaf contains either a true statement or a false statement, and your task is to begin at the one marked 'START', following a continuous line, travelling from leaf to touching leaf, until you reach the one marked 'END'. Every true statement is used in the path from 'START' to 'END', so there are no shortcuts, no paths may cross, nor can any leaf be used twice in order to reach your destination!

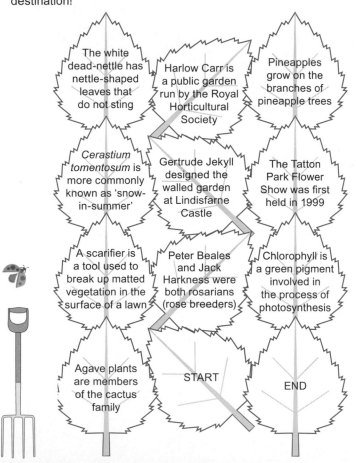

The white dead-nettle has nettle-shaped leaves that do not sting

Harlow Carr is a public garden run by the Royal Horticultural Society

Pineapples grow on the branches of pineapple trees

Cerastium tomentosum is more commonly known as 'snow-in-summer'

Gertrude Jekyll designed the walled garden at Lindisfarne Castle

The Tatton Park Flower Show was first held in 1999

A scarifier is a tool used to break up matted vegetation in the surface of a lawn

Peter Beales and Jack Harkness were both rosarians (rose breeders)

Chlorophyll is a green pigment involved in the process of photosynthesis

Agave plants are members of the cactus family

START

END

See how many of the questions below you can correctly answer.

1 'Amazon', 'Barbados' and 'Lazio' are varieties of which leafy vegetable?

2 What name is given to a mechanical implement used to break up the ground and uproot weeds?

3 The Clover Hill pathway, Modern Courtyard Garden, Catalpa Lawn and Dry Garden are all features of which garden run by the Royal Horticultural Society in Essex?

4 Which of Wales's three national parks lies in the north-west of the country?

5 Which Scottish national park is located approximately twenty miles north of Glasgow?

6 Which plant of the genus *Symphytum*, was formerly used as a 'plaster' to set broken bones?

7 The northern part of which US state is named the Bluegrass region for a grass of the genus *Poa* that grows there?

8 Found floating in the Indian Ocean, a fact that led to its name, which large nut is the fruit of a palm tree (*Lodoicea maldivica*) of the Seychelles?

9 What colour are the berries of the low-growing shrub (*Ruscus aculeatus*) commonly called butcher's broom?

Quotation

No two gardens are the same. No two days are the same in one garden.

Hugh Johnson

See how many of the questions below you can correctly answer.

1   To which family of flowers does vanilla belong?

2   The berries of which evergreen tree are used to add flavour to gin?

3   What are chanterelles and champignons?

4   What is another name for the alligator pear *Persea americana*?

5   What name is given to the plum-like orange edible fruit of a North American tree, *Diospyros virginiana*, of the ebony family?

6   How is the herb *Artemisia dracunculus* better known?

7   Of which fruit is the plantain a subspecies?

8   What type of foodstuff is a habañero?

9   What word is used to describe a fleshy fruit with thin skin and a central stone containing the seed, such as the cherry, almond or olive?

10   Which juicy fruit comes from the tree *Prunus persica*?

Quotation

Plants that wake when others sleep. Timid jasmine buds that keep their fragrance to themselves all day, but when the sunlight dies away let the delicious secret out to every breeze that roams about.

Thomas Moore

Match the silhouettes of the fruiting plants to their names in the list below.

1

2

3

4

5

6

CHERRY **HAWTHORN**
FIG **OLIVE**
GOOSEBERRY **QUINCE**

Honeycomb

Place the letters of each word, one per cell, so that every word flows in a clockwise direction around a number.

Where the hexagons of one word overlap with those of another, the letter in each cell is common to both.

When finished, rearrange the letters in the pale green hexagons to form the name of a flower.

ACROSS

AERIAL

CASING

IRONIC

MYOPIC

POPLAR

PUMICE

QUEASY

SENSOR

STRIVE

SUPPLY

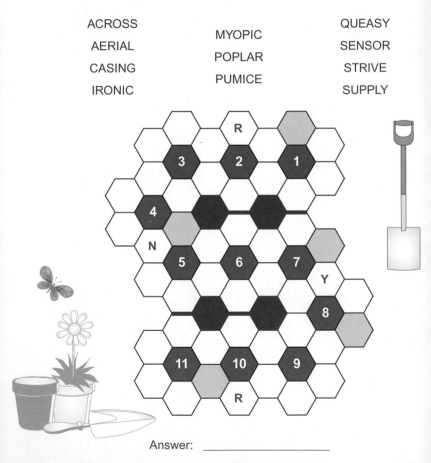

Answer: _____

See how many of the questions below you can correctly answer.

1 Repton is often considered to be the last truly great English garden designer of which century?

2 At the age of 12, Repton was sent by his father to which European country in order to learn the language, regarded as a useful benefit to his father's import and export business?

3 He is generally regarded as being the successor to which earlier landscape gardener?

4 Located within the county of Norfolk, what was Repton's first landscape project?

5 To enable his clients to fully appreciate his intentions, Repton produced manuals containing not only plans but also 'before and after' visuals. What did he call these manuals?

6 One of Repton's commissions was the landscaping and improvements to Plas Newydd. Where is this present-day National Trust site located?

7 For the gardens of which central London square did Repton provide designs in the early 1800s?

8 In 1805, for which Bedfordshire site, the family seat of the Duke of Bedford, did Repton provide designs for the extensive landscaping of the gardens and deer park?

9 With which architect did Repton quarrel when he discovered that the architect had copied his designs for the present-day Brighton Pavilion?

10 In addition to his flair for landscape design, in what art form did Repton also excel?

See how many of the questions below you can correctly answer.

1 Originally published in 1962, which famous landscape gardener wrote *The Education of a Gardener*?

2 "People from a planet without flowers would think we must be mad with joy the whole time to have such things about us." This sentence is taken from *A Fairly Honourable Defeat*, a novel by which author?

3 Who wrote *The Camomile Lawn,* a tale of five cousins who gather in August 1939 for the last summer of their youth?

4 "The drought had lasted now for ten million years and the reign of the terrible lizards had long since ended" is the opening line of which novel?

5 *Rosie*, *Folly* and *The Haunting* are works of fiction by which gardener?

6 *The Darkling Thrush*, *Winter Words* and *Wessex Poems* were written by which poet?

7 What was the title of the book by Charles Darwin regarding his theory of evolution?

8 Which Irish poet wrote *Death of a Naturalist*? He received the 1995 Nobel Prize in Literature.

9 Written by Tom Hart Dyke and Paul Winder, which book of 2011 recounts two backpackers' true story of adventure, survival and extreme horticulture?

Quotation

It is a golden maxim to cultivate the garden for the nose, and the eyes will take care of themselves.

Robert Louis Stevenson

Wordladder

Change one letter at a time (but not the position of any letter) to make a new word – and move from the word at the top of the ladder to the word at the bottom using the exact number of rungs provided.

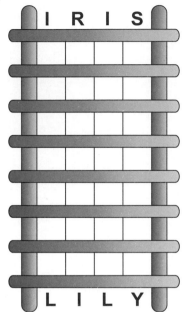

I R I S

L I L Y

True or False

Can you decide whether the statement below is true or false?

Collarette, cactus, pompon, single, show and fancy are just some of many different types of dahlia.

True or **False**

240 Plants in Art

See how many of the questions below you can correctly answer.

1 How many sunflowers are in the vase in the 1888 painting by Vincent van Gogh?

2 *The Garden of Earthly Delights* is a painting on three panels by which Dutch painter?

3 *Coquelicots, La promenade* by Claude Monet is usually known in English-speaking countries by what one-word title?

4 *The Sunflower* is a 1906–07 painting by which Viennese artist?

5 Which kind of flower appears more times than any other in the paintings of Claude Monet?

6 What was the nationality of Judith Leyster, who in 1643 produced her Tulip Book for people who couldn't afford the (at the time) outrageously expensive real thing?

7 In 1882 and in 1883 (the year of his death), which French artist painted a series of pictures of flowers in crystal vases?

8 *The Son of Man* a painting by the Belgian artist Magritte, depicts a man in a bowler hat with his face obscured by which fruit?

9 From 1964 onwards which American artist produced a series of works based on a photograph of four hibiscus blossoms on a grassy background?

10 What kind of bird is on the branch of a cherry tree in Katsushika Hokusai's *… on Branch of Weeping Cherry* of around 1840?

Quotation

I don't like formal gardens. I like wild nature. It's just the wilderness instinct in me, I guess.

Walt Disney

Petal Puzzle

How many words of three or more letters can you make from those on the petals, without using plurals, abbreviations or proper nouns? The central letter must appear once in every word and no letter may be used more than once unless it is on a different petal. There is at least one nine-letter word to be found.

_____
_____
_____
_____
_____
_____
_____

See how many of the questions below you can correctly answer.

1 The yellow fruit, physalis is better known as what?

2 What word is used to describe crushed grapes or juice which is unfermented or partially fermented?

3 What is the North African dish made from durum wheat and water to form small balls?

4 By what name is the cruciferous salad plant *Eruca sativa* better-known?

5 Groundnut oil, used in frying, comes from which nut?

6 What name is given to the cold vegetable soup originating from Spain?

7 Which three main ingredients give the liqueur, kümmel, its distinctive flavour?

8 Which salad, with ingredients including walnuts, celery and apples, gets its name from a New York hotel?

9 By what name is the aubergine better-known in the USA?

10 What is the basic ingredient for the Japanese drink sake?

Quotation

What's a butterfly garden without butterflies?"

Roy Rogers

243 · Garden Borders

Fit the letters G, A, R, D, E and N into the grid in such a way that each horizontal row, each vertical column and each of the heavily bordered sections of six squares contains a different letter. Some letters are already in place.

R			E		
	A				N
		D		N	R
G		N		R	

244 · Trees and Shrubs Tracker

Starting at the top left corner and ending at the bottom right, track a path from letter to letter, in any direction except diagonally, in order to find the hidden trees and shrubs. All of the letters must be used once only.

L	U	R	M	P	L	A	A	N	D	E	R	M	A	H	O	L
A	B	N	U	O	P	R	W	A	L	Y	E	L	P	E	Y	L
L	T	U	N	L	A	W	O	R	T	E	I	L	A	N	W	I
A	U	I	A	S	P	R	I	V	E	W	L	A	L	O	L	L
E	R	S	H	C	U	U	R	P	R	E	E	C	P	W	T	A
L	Z	E	E	D	F	C	U	N	E	L	S	R	O	R	A	M
H	A	L	C	A	R	E	J	I	P	D	E	R	G	I	S	K

217

Spot the Same

Which two cobs of corn are identical in every detail?

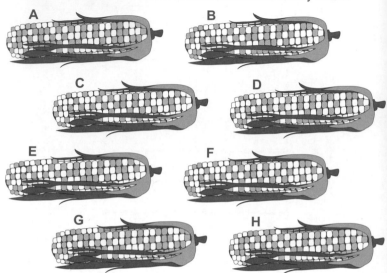

A   B   C   D   E   F   G   H

Spelling Bee

Which is the only one of the following to be correctly spelled?

a   BUDLIEA

b   BUDDLEIA

c   BUDLEIA

d   BUDDLIEA

Find the correct answer to each question from the four alternatives.

1 What is the southern hemisphere equivalent of the aurora borealis?
   a. Aurora antarctis   **b.** Aurora crucis
   c. Aurora australis   **d.** Aurora contraris

2 The term 'lepidoptera' refers to which order of insects?
   a. Beetles   **b.** Butterflies and moths
   c. Spiders   **d.** Flies

3 Found in eastern and southern Africa, what kind of animal is a kudu?
   a. Wild goat   **b.** Wild cat
   c. Vulture   **d.** Antelope

4 Which city in southern Russia shares its name with a kind of soft, tightly-curled lamb's wool used in high-quality clothing?
   a. Astrakhan   **b.** Astana
   c. Yerevan   **d.** Samarkand

5 At 200 plus years, which species of whale has the longest lifespan of any mammal?
   a. Blue whale   **b.** Humpback whale
   c. Sperm whale   **d.** Bowhead whale

6 What term describes a male horse under four years old?
   a. Colt   **b.** Stallion
   c. Foal   **d.** Gelding

7 Gullfoss in Iceland, Tugela in South Africa and Iguazu in Argentina/Brazil are all which type of geographical feature?
   a. Lakes   **b.** Waterfalls
   c. Rivers   **d.** Mountains

See how many of the questions below you can correctly answer.

1 What type of tree is The Capon Tree, one of the last surviving trees from the ancient Jedforest in the Scottish Borders?

2 Due to their lobed appearance, which nuts are called charmarghz (meaning "four brains') in Afghanistan?

3 PVY is a plant virus of the family *Potyviridae*, and one of the most important viruses affecting production of which vegetable?

4 What kind of fruit is a 'pamplemousse' in France?

5 With a name meaning 'hedgehog' or 'sea urchin', what name is given to the prickly plant of the genus *Echinops*, grown in gardens for its attractively rounded heads of pale blue flowers?

6 Which plant, a native of southern Africa, is widely cultivated for its showy pure white spathe and yellow spadix?

7 Which widely-distributed weed (*Capsella bursa-pastoris*) of the cabbage family has white flowers and triangular or heart-shaped seed pods?

8 Traditionally, the log burned as a Yule log in Scotland is from which tree?

9 On which island country in the Indian Ocean is The Avenue (or Alley) of the Baobabs?

Quotation

It is curious, pathetic almost, how deeply seated in the human heart is the liking for gardens and gardening.

Alexander Smith

Garden Maze

How successful will you be in trying to find a route to the centre of this garden maze?

Salad Sudoku

Every row, every column and each of the nine smaller boxes of nine squares should be filled with a different number from 1 to 9 inclusive. Some numbers are already in place. When the grid is completely filled, decode the numbers in the shaded squares, then rearrange the letters to spell out the name of a salad vegetable or fruit.

		7	8			5	1	
				1		6		7
		6		9		8	2	
	9		4					
	7			6			9	
					3		7	
	6	2		4		7		
7		4		3				
	5	1			9	2		

Code

1	2	3	4	5	6	7	8	9
A	E	L	M	N	O	P	R	T

Answer: _____

See how many of the questions below you can correctly answer.

1 Defra is the government department responsible for environmental protection, food production and standards. What is the name of this department, in full?

2 In botany what does the adjective 'ananthous' mean?

3 Scoville units are a method of calibrating the comparative heat of different varieties of what?

4 Latin names of certain plants contain the word *vulgaris*. What is the meaning of *vulgaris*?

5 In botany, what word describes a plant that springs from seed and vegetates one year, then flowers, fructifies and perishes the following year?

6 Often seen in hedgerows, what name is commonly given to *Viburnum lantana*, a large shrub with white flowers and berries that turn red and finally black?

7 Curly, flat-leaf, Japanese and Hamburg are all types of which culinary herb?

8 What word describes a modified leaf or scale, typically small, with a flower or flower cluster in its axil?

9 A sepal is the division of what part of a flower?

Quotation

How fair is a garden amid the trials and passions of existence.

Benjamin Disraeli

Solutions

1

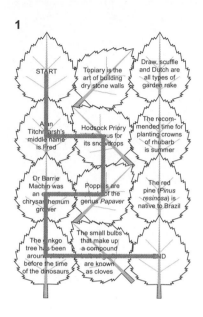

2

1 Sloe, 2 Dianthus, 3 Flora,
4 Trees and shrubs, 5 Yellow,
6 Carl (or Carolus) Linnaeus,
7 St John's wort, 8 Noble and
white, 9 Yew, 10 1960s (1968).

3

1 Bulb, 2 Cornflower, 3 Clematis,
4 Herbs, 5 Dandelion,
6 Pineapple, 7 Damping down,
8 Composts, 9 Seeding and
turfing, 10 Hybrid.

4

1 Lilac,
2 Chestnut,
3 Hawthorn,
4 Acacia,
5 Sugar maple,
6 Rowan.

5

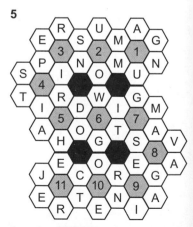

Answer: PEACH

Solutions

6

1 Edelweiss, 2 Berlioz, 3 *Autumn Leaves*, 4 Max Bygraves, 5 *Flowers in the Rain*, 6 Parsley, sage, rosemary, thyme, 7 *The Nutcracker*, 8 The Scaffold, 9 British Airways, 10 *Daisy Daisy* (the original title is *Daisy Bell*).

7

1 Lettuce, 2 Pruning, 3 Grasses, 4 Vitamin A, 5 Opium poppy, 6 Ants, 7 Yellow, 8 Daisy, 9 Houseleek, 10 Australia.

8

Here is one possible solution: PEAR - sear - seam - slam - slum - PLUM

9

False: They are magenta-purple in colour.

10

1 Maple, 2 Cherry, 3 Agave, 4 Celeriac, 5 Watercress, 6 Artichoke, 7 Star fruit, 8 Spinach, 9 Citrus, 10 Clementine.

11

The nine-letter word is: SWEETCORN

12

1 Dock, 2 Deadly nightshade, 3 Angostura, 4 *Myosotis*, 5 Henbane, 6 They are carnivorous, 7 A shoot from the base of a plant, 8 Bergamot, 9 Speedwell, 10 Cowslip.

13

N	R	D	A	E	G
G	D	N	R	A	E
A	E	R	G	D	N
E	G	A	N	R	D
D	A	G	E	N	R
R	N	E	D	G	A

Solutions

14

Anemone, snowdrop, celandine, foxglove, hellebore, cowslip, hyacinth, lilac, daffodil, crocus, fritillary, tulip, violet, freesia, primrose, bluebell.

15

E and H

16

The correctly spelled word is: b

17

1 c, 2 d, 3 b, 4 a, 5 c, 6 d, 7 a.

18

1 Spring, 2 Thrift, 3 Saxifrage, 4 Squirrel, 5 *Gerbera*, 6 Rose, 7 Peas, 8 Urticaria, 9 Rhizome, 10 Cactus (*Cactaceae*).

19

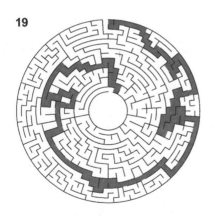

20

3	5	8	1	9	4	2	7	6
6	2	7	3	5	8	9	4	1
1	9	4	6	7	2	8	3	5
8	6	5	2	1	3	7	9	4
4	7	1	5	8	9	6	2	3
2	3	9	4	6	7	5	1	8
7	1	2	8	4	6	3	5	9
5	8	3	9	2	1	4	6	7
9	4	6	7	3	5	1	8	2

Answer: LETTUCE

21

1 Fungi, 2 Oleander, 3 Grafting, 4 Giant bamboo, 5 20 per cent, 6 Myrrh, 7 Insects, 8 Gorse, 9 African violet.

Solutions

22

1 Lawnmower, 2 Beetles,
3 Damselfly, 4 Windflower,
5 No, it is poisonous, 6 Roses,
7 Mulberry, 8 Insects,
9 Gnomon, 10 Black spot.

23

24

Bird = 6, flower = 5, leaf = 4 and mushroom = 3.

25

26

1 Oxfordshire, 2 A straight line, 3 Petworth Park, 4 He hadn't yet "finished England", 5 Croome Court, 6 Humphry Repton, 7 Stowe, 8 George III, 9 Blenheim Palace, 10 Belvoir.

27

1 Cucumber, 2 Methane, 3 Pistil, 4 Thrip, 5 Calendula, 6 Norway, 7 Milfoil, 8 B, 9 Dragonfly, 10 Moth.

28

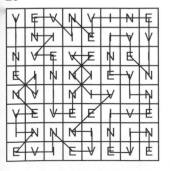

29

1 Plums, 2 Tomato, 3 St John's Wort (or Rose of Sharon), 4 Daddy-long-legs, 5 A spring onion/salad onion, 6 Broccoli, 7 Epsom salts (magnesium sulphate), 8 Salsify, 9 Potassium, 10 Wasp.

Solutions

30
DAISY

31
True.

32
"Help us to be ever faithful gardeners of the spirit, who know that without darkness nothing comes to birth, and without light nothing flowers."

33
1 c, 2 a, 3 a, 4 b, 5 b, 6 c, 7 d, 8 c.

34
1 Rose of Sharon, 2 Mustard, 3 Mint, 4 Moses, 5 Quails, 6 Hyssop, 7 Acacia, 8 Gethsemane, 9 The Hanging Gardens of Babylon, 10 Frankincense.

35

36
1 g,
2 d,
3 a,
4 f,
5 b,
6 h,
7 e,
8 c.

Solutions

37

1 Bats, 2 Nymph, 3 Potato,
4 *Brassica* (or *Brassicaceae*),
5 Daffodil, 6 Summer solstice,
7 Beetles (*Coleoptera*), 8 Fronds,
9 Buttercup, 10 Annuals.

40

B

42

1 b, 2 a, 3 d, 4 c, 5 b, 6 c, 7 d,
8 a.

44

DAFFODIL
PEPPERMINT
WALLFLOWER
HORSERADISH
DOUGLAS FIR
CANTERBURY BELLS
RUNNER BEAN
SWEET PEA

46

1 b, 2 c, 3 c, 4 a, 5 d, 6 c, 7 b,
8 d.

38

1 a, 2 d, 3 b, 4 b, 5 c, 6 c, 7 a,
8 a.

39

1 Hamper (c), 2 Impure (c),
3 Supple (c), 4 Afresh (a),
5 Lethal (c), 6 Hamlet (a).
Answer: THRUSH

41

43

1 Cucumber, 2 Iron, 3 A fungus
of decaying wood, 4 Botanical
tree garden, 5 Ling, 6 Rose,
7 Welsh poppy, 8 A framework
for climbing plants, 9 Fleas,
10 Iris.

45

●	●		●	2	2	2		●	
3		4	2	2	●	●	4	2	
1	●	●	2		3	●	●		0
	3	4	●			2		1	
1	●	2		2			0		0
2			1		●				
●	2			●	2	3	●		0
		●		3	3	3	●	2	0
0	2	2	3	●	●				1
		●			2	2	●	2	●

Solutions

47

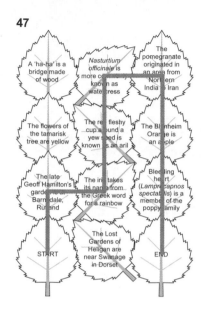

48

1 Lebanese cedar, 2 Laurel,
3 Acacia, 4 Tulip tree, 5 *Prunus*,
6 Carbon dioxide, 7 Eucalyptus,
8 *Ilex*, 9 Chichle, 10 Horseradish tree, 11 Walnut.

49

1 Starling, 2 Finches, 3 Syrinx,
4 Duck, 5 Thrush, 6 Magpie,
7 Woodpecker, 8 Cuckoo,
9 Kookaburra, 10 Pheasant,
11 Heron.

50

1 Lupin,
2 Narcissus,
3 Iris,
4 Nicotiana,
5 Love-lies-bleeding,
6 Astilbe.

51

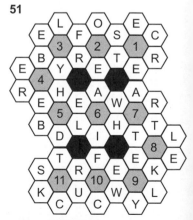

Answer: CELERY

Solutions

52

1 Sir Edwin Lutyens,
2 Connecticut, 3 Impressionism,
4 Somerset, 5 Lindisfarne,
6 South Kensington School of
Art, 7 *Country Life*, 8 Queen
Mary, 9 Royal Horticultural
Society, 10 Godalming.

53

1 Besom, 2 Lichens, 3 Mosses
and liverworts, 4 Botany,
5 Knapweed, 6 Trefoil,
7 Bamboo, 8 A tree (*Eriobotrya
japonica*) or its fruit, 9 Poppy,
10 Hermaphrodite.

54

Here is one possible solution:
NEWT - neat - beat - bent - bend
- bond - POND

55

True.

56

1 Humidity, 2 15 July, 3 Sirocco,
4 Cirrus, 5 Hydrological cycle,
6 Nimbus, 7 The Isles of Scilly,
8 Yellow, 9 Faversham (Kent),
10 Scarlet pimpernel.

57

The nine-letter word is:
HYDRANGEA

58

1 Okra, 2 Borscht, 3 Potatoes,
4 Aniseed, 5 Turnips (or swede)
and potatoes, 6 Paprika,
7 Julienne, 8 Plums, 9 Mezze,
10 Cabbage and potatoes.

59

R	G	A	D	N	E
N	A	E	R	G	D
G	E	D	N	A	R
A	D	G	E	R	N
E	N	R	A	D	G
D	R	N	G	E	A

Solutions

60

Lettuce, cauliflower, broccoli, potato, salsify, celeriac, calabrese, marrow, turnip, carrot, artichoke, radish, parsnip, spinach, onion, cabbage, kale.

61

D and F

62

The correctly spelled word is: c

63

1 c, 2 b, 3 d, 4 b, 5 d, 6 c, 7 a.

64

1 Red, 2 Goldenrod, 3 In the middle of the top (it is a rounded elevation), 4 Foxglove, 5 Shamrock, 6 Turnip, 7 A cereal grass, 8 A bird, 9 Topiary.

65

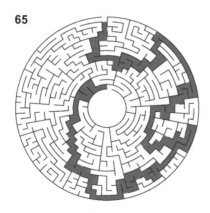

66

6	5	7	3	8	1	9	4	2
4	8	9	7	5	2	6	1	3
2	3	1	4	6	9	5	7	8
8	4	5	1	9	3	7	2	6
9	2	6	8	4	7	3	5	1
1	7	3	5	2	6	4	8	9
5	9	4	6	1	8	2	3	7
3	6	8	2	7	5	1	9	4
7	1	2	9	3	4	8	6	5

Answer: SPRING ONION

67

1 Spider plant, 2 A South American tree, 3 Heather (or heath), 4 Swedes, 5 The Woodland Trust, 6 Pollarding, 7 A bird, 8 Secateurs, 9 Mulch, 10 Greengage.

Solutions

68

1 Cheshire, 2 Pennsylvania,
3 Barnsdale Gardens, 4 The
Cairngorms, 5 Bedgebury
National Pinetum, 6 Tree of
Heaven, 7 The Orto Botanico di
Padova (Padua, Italy), 8 Chelsea
Physic Garden, 9 Yosemite.

69

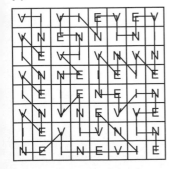

70

Bird = 2, flower = 6, leaf = 5 and
mushroom = 3.

71

72

1 *You Don't Bring Me Flowers*,
2 Donovan, 3 *Penny Lane*,
4 Richard Strauss, 5 Harry
Belafonte, 6 Laurel and Hardy,
7 Edison Lighthouse, 8 Elgar,
9 Buddy Holly, 10 Fir tree,
11 Marv Johnson.

73

1 Snowberry, 2 Division,
3 Red-hot poker (or torch lily),
4 Phloem, 5 Xylem, 6 Snail,
7 A bird, 8 African lily, 9 Norwich
(Norfolk).

74

75

1 Hosta, 2 Augusta National
Golf Club, 3 Yew, 4 Beetle,
5 Dunnock, 6 Orange (orange-
tip butterfly), 7 Bell, 8 Tadpoles,
9 Ferns.

Solutions

76
OLIVE

77
False: it is the scientific study of fungi.

78
"But if each man could have his own house, a large garden to cultivate and healthy surroundings - then, I thought, there will be for them a better opportunity of a happy family life."

79
1 d, 2 d, 3 b, 4 c, 5 c, 6 a, 7 b.

80
1 Narcissus, 2 Yggdrasil,
3 Banyan, 4 Anemone,
5 Chrysanthemum, 6 Demeter,
7 Garlic, 8 Lotus, 9 Hyacinth.

81

82
1 h,
2 e,
3 f,
4 a,
5 c,
6 d,
7 b,
8 g.

Solutions

83

1 Monty Don, 2 *Home Front in the Garden*, 3 *Gardeners' Question Time*, 4 BBC Radio 4, 5 *Life In the Undergrowth*, 6 Carol Klein, 7 *Love Your Garden*, 8 *The Beechgrove Garden*, 9 Carol Kirkwood, 10 Matt James, 11 Charlie Dimmock.

84

1 d, 2 b, 3 a, 4 d, 5 c, 6 b, 7 b, 8 d.

85

1 Famine (a), 2 Fetter (a), 3 Bottle (a), 4 Docile (c), 5 Cinema (a), 6 Tennis (a).
Answer: LINNET

86

A

87

88

1 Dog rose, 2 *Paradise Lost*, 3 William Blake, 4 Maud, 5 Joyce Kilmer, 6 *Among School Children*, 7 William Wordsworth, 8 *Elegy Written in a Country Churchyard*.

89

1 *The Garden of Live Flowers*, 2 Monty Don, 3 *The Wind in the Willows* by Kenneth Grahame, 4 Pemberley, 5 *The Selfish Giant*, 6 *The Roman de la Rose*, 7 Virginia Woolf, 8 *The Scarlet Pimpernel*, 9 William Robinson.

90

ZINNIA
FRENCH BEAN
MOUNTAIN ASH
LONDON PRIDE
GAILLARDIA
HYPERICUM
BOUGAINVILLEA
EUCALYPTUS

91

●		1	●	2	1	2			0
●	3	1	2		●		●		1
●				●	3		1		●
	2	●	3	●	4		2		1
0		1		3	●	●	●		0
1			1	2	●	●	4		
2	●	●				●	4		0
	●		2			●	●		2
		3	●		4	●	5	●	●
	0		●	3	●	●		2	2

92

1 d, 2 b, 3 a, 4 d, 5 c, 6 a, 7 a, 8 d.

Solutions

93

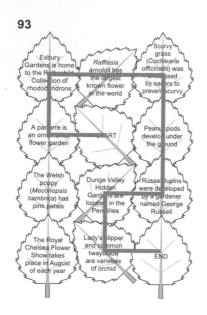

94

1 Grapefruit, 2 Cow parsley,
3 Lonicera (honeysuckle),
4 Frangipani, 5 Rotary hoe
(Rotavator), 6 Yucca, 7 Water
lily, 8 Hover mower, 9 Spadix.

95

1 Samuel Johnson, 2 Vincent
Van Gogh, 3 Cauliflower, 4 Alfred
Russel Wallace, 5 Broccoli,
6 Charles Darwin, 7 Seneca,
8 Edwin Way Teale, 9 Auguste
Rodin, 10 Frank Lloyd Wright.

96

1 Spruce,
2 Birch,
3 Pine,
4 Maple,
5 Oak,
6 Poplar.

97

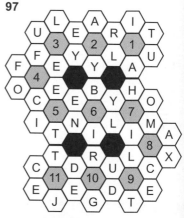

Answer: BEECH

Solutions

98

1 Victoria, 2 Sissinghurst,
3 Novelist and poet, 4 Virginia
Woolf, 5 Knole, 6 White,
7 Rooms, 8 *The Observer*,
9 Sarah Raven, 10 1962.

99

1 Codling moth, 2 Night-scented
stock or evening stock, 3 Cherry,
4 East Malling Research,
5 Algae, 6 A predatory
water bug, 7 Wren, 8 Beetle,
9 Theophrastus.

100

Here is one possible solution:
BUSH - bust - best - beet - feet -
fret - free - TREE

101

True.

102

1 Slug, 2 Orchid, 3 India,
4 White, 5 Hydrangea,
6 Mattock, 7 Meteorology,
8 Cuckoo spit, 9 Solomon's seal.

103

The nine-letter word is:
ARTICHOKE

104

1 Violet-blue, 2 Cabbage, 3 Iris,
4 Ox, 5 The Buckeye State,
6 Lupin, 7 Dig for Victory,
8 Alstroemeria, 9 Damping off.

105

G	A	D	N	R	E
A	E	N	D	G	R
R	N	G	E	D	A
E	G	R	A	N	D
N	D	E	R	A	G
D	R	A	G	E	N

Solutions

106

Greenfly, ladybird, cutworm, shrew, spider, mouse, aphid, mayfly, snail, blackbird, rabbit, thrip, starling, mole, earwig, gnat, sawfly, squirrel, wasp, slug.

107

D and I

108

The correctly spelled word is: a

109

1 a, 2 b, 3 d, 4 c (Red, White, Black, Yellow), 5 d, 6 a, 7 b.

110

1 Mushrooms, 2 Cherry, 3 Scuppernong, 4 Swede, 5 Maize, 6 Cantaloupe melon, 7 Raspberry, 8 Anthophobia, 9 Haricot, 10 Potato.

111

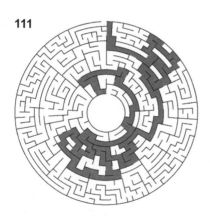

112

2	1	8	7	6	5	9	3	4
3	6	5	4	2	9	8	1	7
7	4	9	8	3	1	6	5	2
5	2	3	6	8	7	1	4	9
8	7	4	1	9	3	5	2	6
1	9	6	2	5	4	3	7	8
6	3	2	5	7	8	4	9	1
4	5	7	9	1	6	2	8	3
9	8	1	3	4	2	7	6	5

Answer: RADISH

113

1 Click beetle, 2 Late autumn or late winter, 3 *Rosa rugosa*, 4 1963, 5 Desiree, 6 Buddleia, 7 Clove, 8 French, 9 Greenhouse effect.

Solutions

114

1 *Singin' in the Rain*,
2 *Lepidoptera*, 3 South America,
4 Pear, 5 Algae (especially
seaweeds), 6 Having crowded,
thick or woolly leaves,
7 The Forestry Commission,
8 Sarsaparilla, 9 Sunflower.

115

116

Bird = 8, flower = 10,
leaf = 11 and mushroom = 2.

117

118

1 Marvin Gaye, 2 Tiny Tim,
3 *The Alamo*, 4 Tom Jones,
5 *Strawberry Fair*, 6 Lilacs,
7 *Blackberry Way*, 8 Herbie
Flowers, 9 Guns N' Roses,
10 Blondie.

119

1 Calendula, 2 Prickles,
3 Anther, 4 Humus, 5 Carrot,
6 Butterfly, 7 Blossom-end rot,
8 Brazil, 9 Rose, 10 White.

120

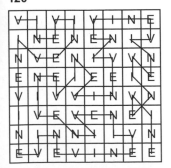

121

1 Apple, 2 Purplish-black,
3 Hydroponics, 4 Mitsuba,
5 Knot garden, 6 Mint, 7 Scots
pine/Scots fir, 8 Raspberry,
9 Truffle.

Solutions

122
ROBIN

123
True.

124
"One lifetime is never enough to accomplish one's horticultural goals. If a garden is a site for the imagination, how can we be very far from the beginning?"

125
1 c, 2 d, 3 a, 4 d, 5 a, 6 b, 7 b, 8 c.

126
1 *The Day of the Triffids*, 2 Alfred Hitchcock, 3 *The Scarlet Pimpernel*, 4 *Steel Magnolias*, 5 *The Death of Grass*, 6 *Driving Miss Daisy*, 7 *The War of the Roses*, 8 Alec Guinness, 9 Doris Day, 10 *The Grapes of Wrath*.

127

128
1 c,
2 e,
3 g,
4 a,
5 d,
6 h,
7 b,
8 f.

Solutions

29

Amber, 2 Pinching out, 3 Teak,
4 Tendril, 5 Margery Fish,
6 Chrysanthemum, 7 Borage,
8 Willow (or *Salicaceae*), 9 Alder.

32

D

134

1 c, 2 a, 3 c, 4 d, 5 b, 6 a, 7 d.

136

HAWTHORN
CORIANDER
ANTIRRHINUM
HELICHRYSUM
COURGETTE
MONKEY PUZZLE
PERIWINKLE
AQUILEGIA

138

1 The Capulets, 2 *A Midsummer
Night's Dream*, 3 *Hamlet*, 4 *The
Winter's Tale*, 5 Cuckooflower,
6 Falstaff, 7 Thee, 8 *King Lear*,
9 *Romeo and Juliet*.

130

1 d, 2 a, 3 d, 4 c, 5 d, 6 b, 7 a,
8 c.

131

1 Alpine (a), 2 Ginger (c),
3 Target (a), 4 Tiptoe (c),
5 Denote (c), 6 Platen (a).
Answer: PIGEON

133

135

1 Sucker, 2 Spindle tree, 3 Black,
4 Letchworth Garden City, 5 New
Jersey, 6 Rue, 7 "Rosebud",
8 Cherries, 9 Nicotiana.

137

0		●	3	●	2	2	●	●	1
1		3	●	2		●		3	
2	●	3			2		3	●	2
4	●			3	●	4	●	4	●
●	●	4		●	●	4	●	4	2
●	●	●	3	●	4			●	2
	4				●		2	4	●
0		●	●	4	●		●		●
	2	●	3	3	●	3			1
		1			1		0		0

Solutions

139

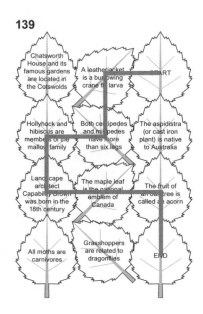

Chatsworth House and its famous gardens are located in the Cotswolds

A leatherjacket is a burrowing crane fly larva

START

Hollyhock and hibiscus are members of the mallow family

Both centipedes and millipedes have more than six legs

The aspidistra (or cast iron plant) is native to Australia

Landscape architect Capability Brown was born in the 18th century

The maple leaf is the national emblem of Canada

The fruit of an oak tree is called an acorn

All moths are carnivores

Grasshoppers are related to dragonflies

END

140

1 Chestnut, 2 Cocoa/cacao,
3 Sesame, 4 Nutmeg,
5 Aniseed, 6 Betel nut,
7 Strawberry, 8 Pecan,
9 Brazil nut.

141

1 North York Moors, 2 Paris,
3 Alexandria, Egypt, 4 Stowe
House, 5 Lullingstone Castle,
6 Yellowstone, 7 Peel Park,
8 Claude Monet, 9 Russia.

142

1 Ash,
2 Willow,
3 Oak,
4 Aspen,
5 Elm,
6 Birch.

143

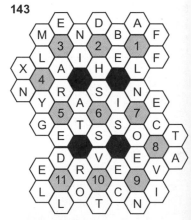

Answer: SALSIFY

Solutions

144

1 *Gardeners' World*, 2 Berlin,
3 *Blue Peter*, 4 MBE,
5 Shrewsbury, 6 Victoria Medal
of Honour, 7 'The Magnolias',
8 *The Daily Mail*, 9 Morecambe
and Wise, 10 Labrador.

145

1 That the person likes butter,
2 Hollyhock, 3 Primrose
(or *Primulaceae*), 4 Japan,
5 Narcissus, 6 Belladonna
lily, 7 Michaelmas daisy,
8 Floriculture, 9 Passion flower
(*Passiflora*), 10 Pansy, 11 Turkey.

146

Here is one possible solution:
FERN - tern - torn - corn - core -
code - rode - ROSE

147

False: It is a member of the
Compositae (or *Asteraceae*)
family. *Ranunculaceae* is the
buttercup family.

148

1 Cloche, 2 The *Flower Pot Men*,
3 Dibber (or dibble), 4 Lavender,
5 Rubber plant, 6 Ontario,
7 Charles I, 8 Pineapple,
9 Honeydew.

149

The nine-letter word is:
SUNFLOWER

150

1 Horsetail, 2 Bird of Paradise
flower, 3 Crab apple, 4 Jersey,
5 Lime, 6 Hyacinth, 7 Latex,
8 Tomato, 9 Deciduous, 10 Red.

151

G	D	E	N	R	A
R	N	D	G	A	E
A	E	N	R	D	G
E	G	A	D	N	R
D	A	R	E	G	N
N	R	G	A	E	D

Solutions

152

Blackberry, pecan, greengage, quince, almond, peach, lemon, gooseberry, pumpkin, raspberry, lime, walnut, melon, cherry, apricot, olive, pear, strawberry.

153

B and G

154

The correctly spelled word is: d

155

1 b, 2 a, 3 c, 4 d, 5 d, 6 c, 7 b.

156

1 Manderley, **2** Oxford's Botanic Garden, **3** *Tom's Midnight Garden*, **4** *The Secret Garden*, **5** *The Merchant's Tale*, **6** *Candide*, **7** Mrs Shears's, **8** San Salvatore.

157

158

3	7	2	4	9	5	1	8	6
4	6	5	1	7	8	9	2	3
8	9	1	3	6	2	7	5	4
5	3	7	2	1	6	8	4	9
1	8	9	5	4	7	3	6	2
6	2	4	8	3	9	5	7	1
9	4	6	7	5	3	2	1	8
7	1	8	9	2	4	6	3	5
2	5	3	6	8	1	4	9	7

Answer: CARROT

159

1 Zucchini, 2 Tartare sauce, 3 Style, 4 Ash-key, 5 Pigs, 6 Canopy, 7 Azalea, 8 Lotus, 9 Pollen.

Solutions

160

1 Quinine, 2 Tamarind, 3 Hazel,
4 Tangerine, orange and
grapefruit, 5 Dutch elm disease,
6 Plums, 7 Pear, 8 Lime,
9 Bougainvillea (Louis Antoine
de Bougainville).

161

162

Bird = 9, flower = 15, leaf = 6 and
mushroom = 12.

163

164

1 Honeysuckle and bindweed,
2 Jean Sibelius, 3 The Lemon
Pipers, 4 Neil Diamond, 5 *He Ain't
Heavy He's My Brother*, 6 Ottorino
Respighi, 7 Dawn, 8 Ivor Novello,
9 Cher, 10 *Honeysuckle Rose*.

165

1 Kumquat, 2 Pink, 3 Busy
Lizzie, 4 Blackcurrant, 5 China,
6 Peas, 7 New Zealand,
8 Longmeadow, 9 *Life in a
Cottage Garden*, 10 Australia.

166

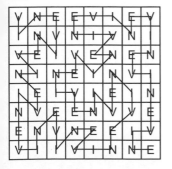

167

1 Mulberry, 2 Invasive,
3 Chinese lantern, 4 South
America, 5 Lettuce, 6 Radish,
7 Humphry Repton, 8 Lebanon,
9 Cabbage.

Solutions

168
TULIP

169
False: it is a cross between a blackberry and a raspberry.

170
"A man has made at least a start on discovering the meaning of human life when he plants shade trees under which he knows full well he will never sit."

171
1 c, 2 a, 3 b, 4 d, 5 c, 6 b, 7 d, 8 a.

172
1 Glasgow, 2 The noble fir (*Abies procera*), 3 Red, 4 Dawyck Botanic Garden, 5 Giant hogweed, 6 The Picton Garden, 7 *Cornus*, 8 Canberra, 9 Plant Heritage, 10 Delphiniums.

173

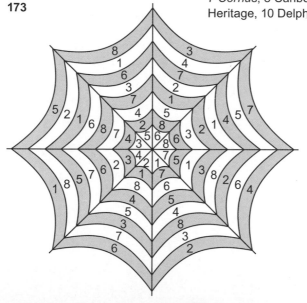

174
1 e,
2 h,
3 f,
4 g,
5 d,
6 b,
7 c,
8 a.

Solutions

75

Australia, 2 Thanet Earth,
3 Harry Wheatcroft, 4 Dill, 5 Red,
6 Dr D G Hessayon, 7 North
America, 8 Sisal, 9 Strawberry.

178

3

180

1 Walt Whitman, 2 *The Two Trees*,
3 William Wordsworth, 4 Tennessee
Williams, 5 The daisy, 6 Francis
Thompson, 7 William Allingham,
8 Robert Burns, 9 Heinrich Heine.

182

TIGER LILY
CAULIFLOWER
HORSE CHESTNUT
GYPSOPHILA
MICHAELMAS DAISY
CELANDINE
JACARANDA
TARRAGON

184

1 c, 2 b, 3 a, 4 d, 5 c, 6 c, 7 a.

176

1 b, 2 c, 3 a, 4 d, 5 a, 6 d, 7 b.

177

1 Menial (c), 2 Mammal (a),
3 Gammon (c), 4 Peking (a),
5 Vipers (c), 6 Vienna (a).
Answer: MAGPIE

179

181

1 Exposure to light (especially
sunlight), 2 Virginia creeper,
3 Bolting, 4 Greenback,
5 Caraway, 6 Sage, 7 Popeye,
8 It is a machine that (or person
who) strips the husks from the
ears of maize, 9 Bouquet garni.

183

1	2				3	●	2	1
●		●	1	●	●	4	●	2
	3	3			5	●		2	●
1	●	3	●	●	●	4			2
	3		●	5	●	●	3	●	1
2	●	●	2			●		4	3
●	5	4		2	3	●	●	●	●
●	5	●	●	●		3	4	6	●
●		●	5		2	2	●		●
	2	2	●	1		●	2	3	●

Solutions

185

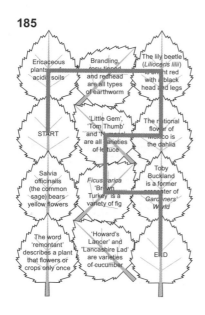

Ericaceous plants enjoy acidic soils

Brandling, gilt, tiger and redhead are all types of earthworm

The lily beetle (*Lilioceris lilii*) is bright red with a black head and legs

START

'Little Gem', 'Tom Thumb' and 'Nymans' are all varieties of lettuce

The national flower of Mexico is the dahlia

Salvia officinalis (the common sage) bears yellow flowers

Ficus carica 'Brown Turkey' is a variety of fig

Toby Buckland is a former presenter of *Gardeners' World*

The word 'remontant' describes a plant that flowers or crops only once

'Howard's Lancer' and 'Lancashire Lad' are varieties of cucumber

END

186

1 15 million, 2 Biogeography,
3 Hops, 4 Cherries,
5 Iceland, 6 Brogdale Farm,
near Faversham (Kent),
7 Phyllomania, 8 Lancelot
'Capability' Brown, 9 Nightjar.

187

1 The Houses of Lancaster
and York, 2 The House of
Lancaster, 3 Idaho, 4 Giant
sequoia (redwood), 5 Hay fever,
6 Powdery mildew, 7 Beetroot,
8 Yellow, 9 Germany.

188

1 Poppy,
2 Bleeding heart,
3 Lily,
4 Tulip,
5 Marigold,
6 Aquilegia.

189

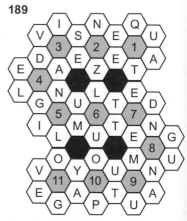

Answer: LOVAGE

248

Solutions

190

1 Ilkley, 2 *Nationwide*, 3 *Ground Force*, 4 *How to Garden*, 5 *Only Dad*, 6 Classic FM, 7 Plant Heritage, 8 Gordon, 9 UKIP, 10 Bastard trenching.

191

1 Morning glory, 2 Swede, 3 Welwyn Garden City, 4 The stalk that joins a leaf to a stem, 5 1804, 6 Orange, 7 Pine, 8 Rocket, 9 Leek.

192

Here is one possible solution:
LEAF - lead - bead - beam - seam - swam - swim - swig - TWIG

193

False: it is native to eastern North America, and was introduced to Europe in the 17th century.

194

1 Geoff Hamilton, 2 Rutland, 3 Grow Wild, 4 Shropshire, 5 Almonds, 6 *Chrysanthemum*, 7 Blackcurrant, 8 Melon, 9 Blue, 10 Yellow.

195

The nine-letter word is: COLUMBINE

196

1 Viola, 2 Aloe vera, 3 Plum, 4 Five, 5 China, 6 Having green flowers, 7 1990, 8 Joe Swift, 9 Toby Buckland, 10 Bear (it's common name is 'bear's ear').

197

A	E	N	R	D	G
N	A	G	D	E	R
R	D	E	G	N	A
D	G	R	N	A	E
E	R	D	A	G	N
G	N	A	E	R	D

Solutions

198

Chervil, comfrey, saffron, tarragon, fennel, camomile, dill, borage, hyssop, lovage, parsley, pepper, sorrel, thyme, endive, sage, mint, angelica, rosemary.

199

C and E

200

The correctly spelled word is: c

201

1 c, 2 d, 3 c, 4 b, 5 b, 6 a, 7 d, 8 b.

202

1 *Leylandii* (the Leyland cypress), 2 Camomile, 3 Peas, 4 Spindle tree, 5 Catmint, 6 Stratification, 7 Blue, 8 Chicory, 9 Gooseberry.

203

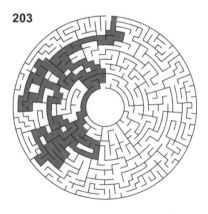

204

5	3	1	9	2	4	8	7	6
8	7	4	6	3	1	2	5	9
6	9	2	7	8	5	1	4	3
9	5	8	3	7	2	6	1	4
4	1	3	5	9	6	7	2	8
7	2	6	1	4	8	9	3	5
2	6	5	4	1	9	3	8	7
3	8	9	2	5	7	4	6	1
1	4	7	8	6	3	5	9	2

Answer: CUCUMBER

205

1 Root, 2 It has hooked hairs that cling to animal fur, 3 Mint (*Lamiaceae*), 4 Cultivar, 5 Carl Linnaeus, 6 Primrose, 7 Coriander, 8 Stinkhorn, 9 Ebony.

Solutions

06

Mr McGregor, 2 The spikes
or prongs of a fork or rake,
3 Australia, 4 Hybrid tea,
5 Yellow, 6 Hardening off, 7 Rye,
8 Pineapple (pineapple weed),
9 Locust.

207

208

Bird = 13, flower = 8,
leaf = 12 and mushroom = 10.

209

210

1 Sting, 2 The Great Plague,
3 "…is impossible to eat",
4 *Poison Ivy*, 5 The Doors, 6 Lyn
Anderson, 7 Johann Strauss II,
8 *Build Me Up Buttercup*, 9 The
Jam, 10 Gustav Mahler.

211

1 Woodpecker, 2 Crows,
3 Mallard, 4 Buzzard, 5 Emu,
6 Tit, 7 Brown, 8 Cuckoo,
9 Robin, 10 A murder, 11 Green
woodpecker, 12 Magpie.

212

213

1 English oak, 2 Cedar,
3 The West Indies, 4 Norway
spruce, 5 Calabash, 6 Rowan,
7 Catkins, 8 Espalier,
9 Hardwoods and softwoods,
10 Elm.

Solutions

214
HOLLY

215
True.

216
"If a person cannot love a plant after he has pruned it, then he has either done a poor job or is devoid of emotion."

217
1 Laurel, 2 Flora, 3 Trees, 4 Mandrake, 5 Clover, 6 Boreas, 7 The asphodel, 8 Vervain, 9 Mistletoe.

218
1 Tom Hart Dyke, 2 David Douglas, 3 Yorkshire, 4 Aimé Bonpland, 5 Sweden, 6 Joseph Banks, 7 Rhododendrons, 8 United States of America, 9 India.

219

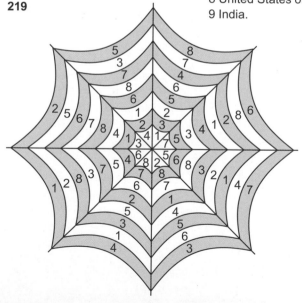

220
1 c,
2 g,
3 e,
4 h,
5 a,
6 d,
7 f,
8 b.

Solutions

1 Elms, 2 Beetle, 3 Sunflower,
4 Swallow, 5 Summer, 6 Chile,
7 Hidcote Manor, 8 Leek,
9 Elder.

224

E

226

1 c, 2 d, 3 b, 4 c, 5 c, 6 d, 7 a,
8 b.

228

NASTURTIUM
WELLINGTONIA
LEMON BALM
PELARGONIUM
CORNFLOWER
MESEMBRYANTHEMUM
ASPARAGUS
SCORZONERA

230

1 d, 2 a (There are many breeds,
but only one species: *Canis
familiaris*), 3 c, 4 a, 5 d, 6 b, 7 d,
8 c.

222

1 c, 2 a, 3 b, 4 d, 5 b, 6 a, 7 c.

223

1 Likely (c), 2 Manila (c),
3 Gdansk (a), 4 Whisky (c),
5 Isaiah (a), 6 Basket (a).
Answer: SISKIN

225

227

1 The Brecon Beacons, 2 Kew
Gardens, 3 Westonbirt Arboretum,
4 Horatio's Garden, 5 The
Tuileries Garden, 6 Hyde Park,
7 Bodnant, 8 The Yorkshire Dales
National Park, 9 The London Eye,
10 Kensington Gardens.

229

2	2		●	2	2	1	2	●	1
●	●	3		●	3	●		2	
		●		2	●	3	4	●	
1	●	4	3			4	●	●	●
	3	●	●	2	●		●	6	●
		●				3		3	●
0			2	●	●	3	1		
	1	1		4	●	●			1
●	2		●	3	3	4	3	●	1
1		●			●		●	2	

Solutions

231

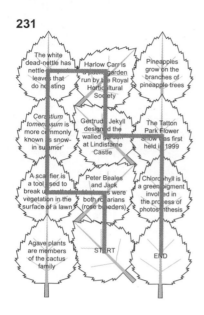

232

1 Spinach, 2 Cultivator (or rotovator), 3 Hyde Hall, 4 Snowdonia National Park, 5 Loch Lomond and Trossachs, 6 Comfrey (knitbone or boneset), 7 Kentucky, 8 Coco-de-mer, 9 Red.

233

1 Orchids, 2 Juniper, 3 Edible fungi, 4 Avocado, 5 Persimmon, 6 Tarragon, 7 Banana, 8 Chilli pepper, 9 Drupe, 10 Peach.

234

1 Fig,
2 Cherry,
3 Olive,
4 Hawthorn,
5 Quince,
6 Gooseberry.

235

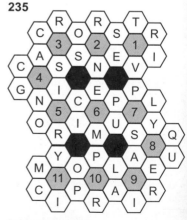

Answer: TULIP